CW00345907

MODERN POETS FOUR

Also edited by Jim Hunter

Modern Poets One
Modern Poets Two
Modern Poets Three
Modern Short Stories

Novels by Jim Hunter

Kinship
Percival and the Presence of God

out of print
The Sun in the Morning
Sally Cray
Earth and Stone
The Flame
Walking in the Painted Sunshine

MODERN POETS FOUR

Revised Edition

Edited by

JIM HUNTER

Headmaster, Weymouth Grammar School

FABER AND FABER

London Boston

First published in 1968
This revised edition published 1979
by Faber and Faber Limited
3 Queen Square London WC1
Printed in Great Britain by
Latimer Trend & Company Ltd Plymouth

British Library Cataloguing in Publication Data

Modern poets
4. – Revised ed.
1. English poetry – 20th century
1. Hunter, Jim
821'.9'1208 PR 1225

ISBN 0-571-04977-x

CONTENTS

INTRODUCTION

This book is one of a series of four, which I really see as a single collection. In these four volumes are printed selections from twenty-two modern poets whose language is English. I have tried to pick the poets that it would be most useful to have in such a collection, but it would be rash to assert that these are the best poets of their time. Simpler to say: here are some recent poets that deserve our attention. Choosing them was not easy. The omission I most regret is that of the Scots poet Hugh MacDiarmid, a controversial figure but one of the most interesting this century: it was felt that the Lallans in which his best work is written would stand too much in the way of readers of this anthology.

Poets are printed here in order of their date of birth. This seemed sounder than attempting to group them according to patterns which not all readers might accept.

More space has been given to some poets than to others. This should not be seen as crude value-judgement—some poets (e.g. D. H. Lawrence) are more discursive than others (e.g. Wallace Stevens). It is true, of course, that where a poet is given an unusual amount of space this is because he seems to me to offer a wide range of distinguished writing, which should be represented as fairly as possible.

There is still more apparent unfairness in the amount of notes supplied for different poets. But this, too, is not in itself a comment on the merit or interest of the poets: some modern writers are straightforward, others are difficult. The space for notes in these books has been kept down, in order to print plenty of poetry; and the notes have had to be confined largely to necessary explanation of difficulties, though I have tried to suggest some critical approaches, and have asked one or two questions to keep the reader awake.

In writing the notes I have, of course, drawn freely on various critical works, biographies and commentaries. The notes are intended to be simple and minimal; and anyone seriously studying the poets will need to read about their work and lives for himself. In choosing poets and poems, and in writing the notes, I have been helped by conversation with a number of friends, and in particular by Frank Beecroft, Bill Haxworth, Fred Inglis, and Andor Gomme.

INTRODUCTION TO REVISED EDITION

MODERN POETS appeared in 1968. The first three volumes will continue to be printed, but the original Volume Four is now out of date, because the poets included there have done far more work since. The revised MODERN POETS FOUR will be followed by an entirely new Volume Five, which will feature poets who have made their reputation during the last ten years.

In revising Volume Four I have (reluctantly) left out two poets previously included, because the claims of Sylvia Plath and Thom Gunn now seem stronger. From the other four poets a new selection has been made. It has been exciting to see the development of these poets within the last ten years, and this book certainly seems to me now far stronger and more challenging.

I am grateful to Charles Tomlinson for reading my draft notes on his poetry and clarifying some details.

JIM HUNTER

Philip Larkin

Philip Larkin was born in 1922 and brought up in Coventry. He was educated at Oxford, and since then has had various posts as a librarian. He is now librarian of the University of Hull. He has published four books of poetry and two novels.

Larkin is one of the most popular poets of today, for his clarity and honesty. He is an extreme version of the 1950s anti-hero: visiting a church he doesn't even give a valid sixpence, he is sardonic at the expense (as it seems) of religious faith, marriage, family and (by implication) of literary pretension also, for he writes in a prosaic colloquial manner and is never obscure. His subject-matter is faceless urban civilization and a faceless people: a world of defeat, tawdriness and suppressed or under-developed emotions. The odd thing is that he seems to relish all this, rather as the even more popular John Betjeman relishes the world of the *Daily Telegraph* reader.

What Larkin really relishes, perhaps, is the notion of human dignity even when the life seems tawdry. A church is a precious place, marriage a noble change, even in the eyes of atheist and bachelor. Larkin's more recent poetry is increasingly bitter about the collapse of values and the loss of traditional unpretentious beauty (GOING, GOING); and its few happier notes are reserved for such traditions as continue (SHOW SATURDAY—the poet's old relish comes through) or for the basic family solidarity described in TO THE SEA.

The special flavour of Larkin's poetry is a combination of the flattest kind of realism with hints of an ancient poetic grandeur. His journalistic sketching is done in traditional meditative verse-forms, and done without apparent effort—sometimes, indeed, with grace. The conclusions of key poems are abstract, generalized, and metaphysical (in the sense of being about life and death, no less). Much of what is best and worst in modern England may be seen in Larkin's poetry—not only in its content, but in the mixture of apathetic non-involvement and a nostalgia for old goodness. Critics of Larkin might say that the sort of laziness and scepticism which his poetry has often represented are partly responsible for the decline he so much laments. Of course Larkin knows this: he is at all times painstakingly self-critical.

Wedding-Wind

The wind blew all my wedding-day,
And my wedding-night was the night of the high wind;
And a stable door was banging, again and again,
That he must go and shut it, leaving me
Stupid in candlelight, hearing rain,
Seeing my face in the twisted candlestick,
Yet seeing nothing. When he came back
He said the horses were restless, and I was sad
That any man or beast that night should lack
The happiness I had.

Now in the day
All's ravelled under the sun by the wind's blowing.
He has gone to look at the floods, and I
Carry a chipped pail to the chicken-run,
Set it down, and stare. All is the wind
Hunting through clouds and forests, thrashing
My apron and the hanging cloths on the line.
Can it be borne, this bodying-forth by wind
Of joy my actions turn on, like a thread
Carrying beads? Shall I be let to sleep
Now this perpetual morning shares my bed?
Can even death dry up
These new delighted lakes, conclude
Our kneeling as cattle by all-generous waters?

Church-Going

Once I am sure there's nothing going on
I step inside, letting the door thud shut.
Another church: matting, seats, and stone,
And little books; sprawlings of flowers, cut
For Sunday, brownish now; some brass and stuff
Up at the holy end; the small neat organ;
And a tense, musty, unignorable silence,
Brewed God knows how long. Hatless, I take off
My cycle-clips in awkward reverence,

Move forward, run my hand around the font.
From where I stand, the roof looks almost new—
Cleaned, or restored? Someone would know: I don't.
Mounting the lectern, I peruse a few
Hectoring large-scale verses, and pronounce
'Here endeth' much more loudly than I'd meant.
The echoes snigger briefly. Back at the door
I sign the book, donate an Irish sixpence,
Reflect the place was not worth stopping for.

Yet stop I did: in fact I often do,
And always end much at a loss like this,
Wondering what to look for; wondering, too,
When churches fall completely out of use
What we shall turn them into, if we shall keep
A few cathedrals chronically on show,
Their parchment, plate, and pyx in locked cases,
And let the rest rent-free to rain and sheep.
Shall we avoid them as unlucky places?

Or, after dark, will dubious women come
To make their children touch a particular stone;
Pick simples for a cancer; or on some
Advised night see walking a dead one?
Power of some sort or other will go on
In games, in riddles, seemingly at random;
But superstition, like belief, must die,
And what remains when disbelief has gone?
Grass, weedy pavement, brambles, buttress, sky,

A shape less recognizable each week,
A purpose more obscure. I wonder who
Will be the last, the very last, to seek
This place for what it was; one of the crew
That tap and jot and know what roodlofts were?
Some ruin-bibber, randy for antique,
Or Christmas-addict, counting on a whiff
Of gown-and-bands and organ-pipes and myrrh?
Or will he be my representative,

Bored, uninformed, knowing the ghostly silt
Dispersed, yet tending to this cross of ground
Through suburb scrub because it held unspilt
So long and equably what since is found
Only in separation—marriage, and birth,
And death, and thoughts of these—for which was built
This special shell? For, though I've no idea
What this accoutred frowsty barn is worth,
It pleases me to stand in silence here;

A serious house on serious earth it is,
In whose blent air all our compulsions meet,
Are recognized, and robed as destinies.

And that much never will be obsolete,
Since someone will for ever be surprising
A hunger in himself to be more serious,
And gravitating with it to this ground,
Which, he once heard, was proper to grow wise in,
If only that so many dead lie round.

The Whitsun Weddings

That Whitsun, I was late getting away:
    Not till about
One-twenty on the sunlit Saturday
Did my three-quarters-empty train pull out,
All windows down, all cushions hot, all sense
Of being in a hurry gone. We ran
Behind the backs of houses, crossed a street
Of blinding windscreens, smelt the fish-dock; thence
The river's level drifting breadth began,
Where sky and Lincolnshire and water meet.

All afternoon, through the tall heat that slept
    For miles inland,
A slow and stopping curve southwards we kept.
Wide farms went by, short-shadowed cattle, and
Canals with floatings of industrial froth;
A hothouse flashed uniquely: hedges dipped
And rose: and now and then a smell of grass
Displaced the reek of buttoned carriage-cloth
Until the next town, new and nondescript,
Approached with acres of dismantled cars.

At first, I didn't notice what a noise
        The weddings made
Each station that we stopped at: sun destroys
The interest of what's happening in the shade,
And down the long cool platforms whoops and skirls
I took for porters larking with the mails,
And went on reading. Once we started, though,
We passed them, grinning and pomaded, girls
In parodies of fashion, heels and veils,
All posed irresolutely, watching us go,

As if out on the end of an event
        Waving goodbye
To something that survived it. Struck, I leant
More promptly out next time, more curiously,
And saw it all again in different terms:
The fathers with broad belts under their suits
And seamy foreheads; mothers loud and fat;
An uncle shouting smut; and then the perms,
The nylon gloves and jewellery-substitutes,
The lemons, mauves, and olive-ochres that

Marked off the girls unreally from the rest.
        Yes, from cafés
And banquet-halls up yards, and bunting-dressed
Coach-party annexes, the wedding-days
Were coming to an end. All down the line
Fresh couples climbed aboard: the rest stood round;
The last confetti and advice were thrown,
And, as we moved, each face seemed to define
Just what it saw departing: children frowned
At something dull; fathers had never known

Success so huge and wholly farcical;
The women shared
The secret like a happy funeral;
While girls, gripping their handbags tighter, stared
At a religious wounding. Free at last,
And loaded with the sum of all they saw,
We hurried towards London, shuffling gouts of steam.
Now fields were building-plots, and poplars cast
Long shadows over major roads, and for
Some fifty minutes, that in time would seem

Just long enough to settle hats and say
I nearly died,
A dozen marriages got under way.
They watched the landscape, sitting side by side
—An Odeon went past, a cooling tower,
And someone running up to bowl—and none
Thought of the others they would never meet
Or how their lives would all contain this hour.
I thought of London spread out in the sun,
In postal districts packed like squares of wheat:

There we were aimed. And as we raced across
Bright knots of rail
Past standing Pullmans, walls of blackened moss
Came close, and it was nearly done, this frail
Travelling coincidence; and what it held
Stood ready to be loosed with all the power
That being changed can give. We slowed again,
And as the tightened brakes took hold, there swelled
A sense of falling, like an arrow-shower
Sent out of sight, somewhere becoming rain.

MCMXIV

Those long uneven lines
Standing as patiently
As if they were stretched outside
The Oval or Villa Park,
The crowns of hats, the sun
On moustached archaic faces
Grinning as if it were all
An August Bank Holiday lark;

And the shut shops, the bleached
Established names on the sunblinds,
The farthings and the sovereigns,
And dark-clothed children at play
Called after kings and queens,
The tin advertisements
For cocoa and twist, and the pubs
Wide open all day;

And the countryside not caring:
The place-names all hazed over
With flowering grasses, and fields
Shadowing Doomsday lines
Under wheat's restless silence;
The differently-dressed servants
With tiny rooms in huge houses,
The dust behind limousines;

Never such innocence,
Never before or since,
As changed itself to past
Without a word—the men
Leaving the gardens tidy,
The thousands of marriages
Lasting a little while longer:
Never such innocence again.

Ambulances

Closed like confessionals, they thread
Loud noons of cities, giving back
None of the glances they absorb.
Light glossy grey, arms on a plaque,
They come to rest at any kerb:
All streets in time are visited.

Then children strewn on steps or road,
Or women coming from the shops
Past smells of different dinners, see
A wild white face that overtops
Red stretcher-blankets momently
As it is carried in and stowed,

And sense the solving emptiness
That lies just under all we do,
And for a second get it whole,
So permanent and blank and true.
The fastened doors recede. *Poor soul,*
They whisper at their own distress;

For borne away in deadened air
May go the sudden shut of loss
Round something nearly at an end,
And what cohered in it across
The years, the unique random blend
Of families and fashions, there

At last begin to loosen. Far
From the exchange of love to lie
Unreachable inside a room
The traffic parts to let go by
Brings closer what is left to come,
And dulls to distance all we are.

To the Sea

To step over the low wall that divides
Road from concrete walk above the shore
Brings sharply back something known long before—
The miniature gaiety of seasides.
Everything crowds under the low horizon:
Steep beach, blue water, towels, red bathing caps,
The small hushed waves' repeated fresh collapse
Up the warm yellow sand, and further off
A white steamer stuck in the afternoon—

Still going on, all of it, still going on!
To lie, eat, sleep in hearing of the surf
(Ears to transistors, that sound tame enough
Under the sky), or gently up and down

Lead the uncertain children, frilled in white
And grasping at enormous air, or wheel
The rigid old along for them to feel
A final summer, plainly still occurs
As half an annual pleasure, half a rite,

As when, happy at being on my own,
I searched the sand for Famous Cricketers,
Or, farther back, my parents, listeners
To the same seaside quack, first became known.
Strange to it now, I watch the cloudless scene:
The same clear water over smoothed pebbles,
The distant bathers' weak protesting trebles
Down at its edge, and then the cheap cigars,
The chocolate-papers, tea-leaves, and, between

The rocks, the rusting soup-tins, till the first
Few families start the trek back to the cars.
The white steamer has gone. Like breathed-on glass
The sunlight has turned milky. If the worst
Of flawless weather is our falling short,
It may be that through habit these do best,
Coming to water clumsily undressed
Yearly; teaching their children by a sort
Of clowning; helping the old, too, as they ought.

Show Saturday

Grey day for the Show, but cars jam the narrow lanes.
Inside, on the field, judging has started: dogs
(Set their legs back, hold out their tails) and ponies
(manes
Repeatedly smoothed, to calm heads); over there,
sheep
(Cheviot and Blackface); by the hedge, squealing logs
(Chain Saw Competition). Each has its own keen crowd.
In the main arena, more judges meet by a jeep:
The jumping's on next. Announcements, splutteringly
loud,

Clash with the quack of a man with pound notes round
his hat
And a lit-up board. There's more than just animals:
Bead-stalls, balloon-men, a Bank; a beer-marquee that
Half-screens a canvas Gents; a tent selling tweed,
And another, jackets. Folks sit about on bales
Like great straw dice. For each scene is linked by spaces
Not given to anything much, where kids scrap, freed,
While their owners stare different ways with incurious
faces.

The wrestling starts, late; a wide ring of people; then
cars;
Then trees; then pale sky. Two young men in acrobats'
tights
And embroidered trunks hug each other; rock over the
grass,
Stiff-legged, in a two-man scrum. One falls: they shake
hands.

Two more start, one grey-haired: he wins, though.
They're not so much fights
As long immobile strainings that end in unbalance
With one on his back, unharmed, while the other stands
Smoothing his hair. But there are other talents—

The long high tent of growing and making, wired-off
Wood tables past which crowds shuffle, eyeing the
scrubbed spaced
Extrusions of earth: blanch leeks like church candles,
six pods of
Broad beans (one split open), dark shining-leafed
cabbages—rows
Of single supreme versions, followed (on laced
Paper mats) by dairy and kitchen; four brown eggs, four
white eggs,
Four plain scones, four dropped scones, pure excellences
that enclose
A recession of skills. And, after them, lambing-sticks,
rugs,

Needlework, knitted caps, baskets, all worthy, all well
done,
But less than the honeycombs. Outside, the jumping's
over.
The young ones thunder their ponies in competition
Twice round the ring; then trick races, Musical Stalls,
Sliding off, riding bareback, the ponies dragged to and
fro for
Bewildering requirements, not minding. But now, in the
background,
Like shifting scenery, horse-boxes move; each crawls
Towards the stock entrance, tilting and swaying, bound

For far-off farms. The pound-note man decamps.
The car park has thinned. They're loading jumps on a
truck.
Back now to private addresses, gates and lamps
In high stone one-street villages, empty at dusk,
And side roads of small towns (sports finals stuck
In front doors, allotments reaching down to the railway);
Back now to autumn, leaving the ended husk
Of summer that brought them here for Show Saturday—

The men with hunters, dog-breeding wool-defined
women,
Children all saddle-swank, mugfaced middleaged wives
Glaring at jellies, husbands on leave from the garden
Watchful as weasels, car-tuning curt-haired sons—
Back now, all of them, to their local lives:
To names on vans, and business calendars
Hung up in kitchens; back to loud occasions
In the Corn Exchange, to market days in bars,

To winter coming, as the dismantled Show
Itself dies back into the area of work.
Let it stay hidden there like strength, below
Sale-bills and swindling; something people do,
Not noticing how time's rolling smithy-smoke
Shadows much greater gestures; something they share
That breaks ancestrally each year into
Regenerate union. Let it always be there.

Going, Going

I thought it would last my time—
The sense that, beyond the town,
There would always be fields and farms,
Where the village louts could climb
Such trees as were not cut down;
I knew there'd be false alarms

In the papers about old streets
And split-level shopping, but some
Have always been left so far;
And when the old part retreats
As the bleak high-risers come
We can always escape in the car.

Things are tougher than we are, just
As earth will always respond
However we mess it about;
Chuck filth in the sea, if you must:
The tides will be clean beyond.
—But what do I feel now? Doubt?

Or age, simply? The crowd
Is young in the M1 café;
Their kids are screaming for more—
More houses, more parking allowed,
More caravan sites, more pay.
On the Business Page, a score

Of spectacled grins approve
Some takeover bid that entails
Five per cent profit (and ten

Per cent more in the estuaries): move
Your works to the unspoilt dales
(Grey area grants)! And when

You try to get near the sea
In summer . . .
                    It seems, just now,
To be happening so very fast;
Despite all the land left free
For the first time I feel somehow
That it isn't going to last,

That before I snuff it, the whole
Boiling will be bricked in
Except for the tourist parts—
First slum of Europe: a role
It won't be so hard to win,
With a cast of crooks and tarts.

And that will be England gone,
The shadows, the meadows, the lanes,
The guildhalls, the carved choirs.
There'll be books; it will linger on
In galleries; but all that remains
For us will be concrete and tyres.

Most things are never meant.
This won't be, most likely: but greeds
And garbage are too thick-strewn
To be swept up now, or invent
Excuses that make them all needs.
I just think it will happen, soon.

Notes

WEDDING-WIND

In this early poem, the poet writes in the person of a girl newly married to a farmer. This fictional framework enables him to write more lyrically and energetically than usual. Look at the lively verse-movement.

CHURCH-GOING

py: vessel in which consecrated bread is kept.

simples: medicinal herbs.

accoutred: cluttered.

blent: blended. See the previous verse: because it held unspilt/So long and equably what since is found/Only in separation . . .

A key poem of Larkin's: basically, the poet—like many of us—wants it both ways.

THE WHITSUN WEDDINGS

Larkin shares with some novelists the gift of capturing humdrum reality vividly on the page. The poet here is not an august literary personage on a different level from ourselves: on the contrary, supposing we travelled south from Hull one Whit Saturday a few years ago, we were perhaps in the same compartment with him. The windscreens, the industrial froth, the man running up to bowl, the 'major roads'—these make the background of the poem real, and the foreground (the weddings) has the more urgency. True, nowadays most people have a car to hop into after their wedding; and this particular sharing (like so many others) now no longer occurs.

Don't let the skilful ease of the writing make you skim over the poem's thought. 'Difficult' poems are not necessarily any more subtle or delicate than this!

MCMXIV

The poet has been looking at photographs of 1914—men queuing up to enlist in the war. The last verse is not frivolous: its idea is one many commentators would endorse—that those days of 1914, before the real scale and nature of world war had been realized, were the last of this illusion and innocence.

AMBULANCES

In modern urban life, we tend to forget about death. The shock of seeing the ambulance restores a true scale of values to us; 'for a second' we 'get it whole': our death seems real to us again, our present lives almost irrelevant.

TO THE SEA

The family seaside holiday was an immensely strong English tradition, at its height perhaps in Larkin's between-the-wars childhood. He is surprised and, mostly, delighted to find the tradition still alive.

Famous Cricketers: picture-cards issued with cigarette packets (more common with cereals today).

SHOW SATURDAY

The annual Show is still (Larkin is happy to find) a big event in many North Country market towns, and one of its most attractive aspects is its inclusiveness. Compare CHURCH-GOING—'what since is found/Only in separation'. Such inclusiveness of trade, many kinds of sport, domestic pride, and sheer fun is itself respectful of people and their diversity. And such respect is moral strength 'below/Sale-bills and swindling'.

GOING, GOING

Commissioned by the Department of the Environment. A characteristically deft mixture of bald colloquialism and a lilting, rhyming verse. There is plenty here to think about, both about the spread of 'greeds and garbage' and about the apathy which makes such spread possible. Perhaps if people of Larkin's views had *acted* more, instead of hoping 'it would last my time' . . . think what selfishness is implied here.

Charles Tomlinson

Charles Tomlinson was born at Stoke-on-Trent in 1927. He read English at Cambridge, and was a schoolteacher and private secretary before becoming a university teacher. He lectures in English at the University of Bristol, and has also taught in New Mexico. He has published nine books of poetry.

Tomlinson's reputation grew quietly, but it will probably outlast many more suddenly gained. He writes precisely, and with the deepest respect for language—which means that sometimes the long and unfamiliar word is the only exactly right one. If his poetry seems difficult, you are probably hurrying it: follow the sentence structure meticulously, as the poet himself does, and the statement is then seen to be as clearly put as one could wish—though it may well still be an *intellectual* statement, and Tomlinson would see nothing wrong in that. Hurrying may also cause you to miss the artistry of the verse-movement and the internal rhymes. Tomlinson's poems move like a quiet snooker game: what seems like an uneasy and even uncertain touch clicks to a magical outcome of calm. Read them aloud.

The old word 'aesthetic' may be used to suggest Tomlinson's view of poetry. Even when a poem most preaches (as in AGAINST EXTREMITY) it must be made and shaped: it is a work of art, not a piece of propaganda or philosophy. This is apparent in Tomlinson's delicate verse and dry humour of verbal echo; but also in his conscious links with visual art—he is in fact increasingly becoming known as a painter as well as a poet, and the last poem in this selection (RHYMES) sums up his achievement. There is no lack of ideas, of course—some might even call Tomlinson a religious poet. But his moral comment or philosophy is folded into the work of art, the poem: then it becomes the reader's as much as the poet's, and can be looked at from several sides.

How Still the Hawk

How still the hawk
Hangs innocent above
Its native wood:
Distance, that purifies the act
Of all intent, has graced
Intent with beauty.
Beauty must lie
As innocence must harm
Whose end (sited,
Held) is naked
Like the map it cowers on.
And the doom drops:
Plummet of peace
To him who does not share
The nearness and the need,
The shrivelled circle
Of magnetic fear.

Winter Encounters

House and hollow; village and valley-side:
    The ceaseless pairings; the interchange
In which the properties are constant
    Resumes its winter starkness. The hedges' barbs
Are bared. Lengthened shadows
    Intersecting, the fields seem parcelled smaller
As if by hedgerow within hedgerow. Meshed
    Into neighbourhood by such shifting ties,
The house reposes, squarely upon its acre
    Yet with softened angles, the responsive stone
Changeful beneath the changing light:
    There is a riding-forth, a voyage impending
In this ruffled air, where all moves
    Towards encounter. Inanimate or human,
The distinction fails in these brisk exchanges—
    Say, merely, that the roof greets the cloud,
Or by the wall, sheltering its knot of talkers,
    Encounter enacts itself in the conversation
On customary subjects, where the mind
    May lean at ease, weighing the prospect
Of another's presence. Rain
    And the probability of rain, tares
And their progress through a field of wheat—
    These, though of moment in themselves,
Serve rather to articulate the sense
    That having met, one meets with more
Than the words can witness. One feels behind
    Into the intensity that bodies through them
Calmness within the wind, the warmth in cold.

What it was like

It was like the approach of flame
treading the tinder, a fleet
cascade of it taking tree-toll,
halting below the hill and then
covering the corn-field's dryness
in an effortless crescendo. One heard
in the pause of the receding silence
the whole house grow
tense through its ties, the beams
brace beneath pan-tiles
for the coming burst. It came
and went. The blinded pane
emerged from the rainsheet
to an after-water world,
its green confusion brought
closer greener. The baptism
of the shining house was done
and it was like the calm
a church aisle harbours
tasting of incense, space and stone.

How it happened

It happened like this: I heard
from the farm beyond, a grounded
churn go down. The sound
chimed for the wedding of the mind
with what one could not see,
the further fields, the seamless
spread of space, and then,
all bestial ease, the cows
foregathered by the milking place
in a placid stupor. There are two
ways to marry with a land—
first, this bland and blind
submergence of the self, an act
of kind and questionless. The other
is the thing I mean, a whole
event, a happening, the sound
that brings all space in
for its bound, when self is clear
as what we keenest see and hear:
no absolute of eye can tell
the utmost, but the glance
goes shafted from us like a well.

The Weathercocks

Bitten and burned into mirrors of thin gold,
the weathercocks, blind from the weather,
have their days of seeing as they
grind round on their swivels.

A consciousness of pure metal
begins to melt when (say)
that light 'which never was'
begins to be

And catches the snow's accents
in each dip and lap, and the wide
stains on the thawed ploughland are like continents
across a rumpled map.

Their gold eyes hurt
at the corduroy lines come clear whose grain
feels its way over the shapes of the rises
joining one brown accord of stain and stain.

And the patterning stretches, flown
out on a wing of afternoon cloud that the sun
is changing to sea-wet sandflats,
hummocked in tiny dunes like the snow half-gone

As if the sole wish of the light
were to harrow mind with matter, to shock
wide the glance of the tree-knots and the stone-eyes
the sun is bathing, to waken the weathercocks.

On a Mexican Straw Christ

This is not the event. This
Is a man of straw,
The legs straw-thin
The straw-arms shent
And nailed. And yet this dry
Essence of agony must be
Close-grained to the one
They lifted down, when
Consummatum est the event was done.
Below the baroque straw-
Haloed basket-head
And the crown, far more
Like a cap woven
For a matador than a crown of thorns,
A gap recedes: it makes
A mouth in pain, the teeth
Within its sideways-slashed
And gritted grin, are
Verticals of straw, and they
Emerge where the mask's
Chin ceases and become
Parallels plunging down, their sum
The body of God. Beneath,
Two feet join in one
Cramped culmination, as if
To say: 'I am the un-
Resurrection and the Death.'

Swimming Chenango Lake

Winter will bar the swimmer soon.
  He reads the water's autumnal hesitations
A wealth of ways: it is jarred,
  It is astir already despite its steadiness,
Where the first leaves at the first
  Tremor of the morning air have dropped
Anticipating him, launching their imprints
  Outwards in eccentric, overlapping circles.
There is a geometry of water, for this
  Squares off the clouds' redundances
And sets them floating in a nether atmosphere
  All angles and elongations: every tree
Appears a cypress as it stretches there
  And every bush that shows the season,
A shaft of fire. It is a geometry and not
  A fantasia of distorting forms, but each
Liquid variation answerable to the theme
  It makes away from, plays before:
It is a consistency, the grain of the pulsating flow.
  But he has looked long enough, and now
Body must recall the eye to its dependence
  As he scissors the waterscape apart
And sways it to tatters. Its coldness
  Holding him to itself, he grants the grasp,
For to swim is also to take hold
  On water's meaning, to move in its embrace
And to be, between grasp and grasping, free.
  He reaches in-and-through to that space
The body is heir to, making a where
  In water, a possession to be relinquished
Willingly at each stroke. The image he has torn

Flows-to behind him, healing itself,
Lifting and lengthening, splayed like the feathers
Down an immense wing whose darkening spread
Shadows his solitariness: alone, he is unnamed
By this baptism, where only Chenango bears a name
In a lost language he begins to construe—
A speech of densities and derisions, of half-
Replies to the questions his body must frame
Frogwise across the all but penetrable element.
Human, he fronts it and, human, he draws back
From the interior cold, the mercilessness
That yet shows a kind of mercy sustaining him.
The last sun of the year is drying his skin
Above a surface a mere mosaic of tiny shatterings,
Where a wind is unscaping all images in the flowing obsidian,
The going-elsewhere of ripples incessantly shaping.

Against Extremity

Let there be treaties, bridges,
  Chords under the hands, to be spanned
Sustained: extremity hates a given good
  Or a good gained. That girl who took
Her life almost, then wrote a book
  To exorcise and to exhibit the sin,
Praises a friend there for the end she made
  And each of them becomes a heroine.
The time is in love with endings. The time's
  Spoiled children threaten what they will do,
And those they cannot shake by petulance
  They'll bribe out of their wits by show.
Against extremity, let there be
  Such treaties as only itime tself
Can ratify, a bond and test
  Of sequential days, and like the full
Moon slowly given to the night,
  A possession that is not to be possessed.

A Sense of Distance

The door is shut.
The red rider
no longer crosses the canyon floor
under a thousand feet of air.

The glance that fell
on him, is shafting
a deeper well:
the boughs of the oak are roaring
inside the acorn shell.

The hoofbeats—silent, then—
are sounding now
that ride
dividing a later distance.

For I am in England,
and the mind's embrace
catches-up this English
and that horizonless desert space
into its own, and the three there
concentrically fill a single sphere.

And it seems as if a wind
had flung wide a door
above an abyss, where all
the kingdoms of possibilities shone
like sandgrains crystalline in the mind's own sun.

The Chances of Rhyme

The chances of rhyme are like the chances of meeting—
In the finding fortuitous, but once found, binding:
They say, they signify and they succeed, where to succeed
Means not success, but a way forward
If unmapped, a literal, not a royal succession;
Though royal (it may be) is the adjective or region
That we, nature's royalty, are led into.
Yes. We are led, though we seem to lead
Through a fair forest, an Arden (a rhyme
For Eden)—breeding ground for beasts
Not bestial, but loyal and legendary, which is more
Than nature's are. Yet why should we speak
Of art, of life, as if the one were all form
And the other all Sturm-und-Drang? And I think
Too, we should confine to Crewe or to Mow
Cop, all those who confuse the fortuitousness
Of art with something to be met with only
At extremity's brink, reducing thus
Rhyme to a kind of rope's end, a glimpsed grass
To be snatched at as we plunge past it—
Nostalgic, after all, for a hope deferred.
To take chances, as to make rhymes
Is human, but between chance and impenitence
(A half-rhyme) come dance, vigilance
And circumstance (meaning all that is there
Besides you, when you are there). And between
Rest-in-peace and precipice,
Inertia and perversion, come the varieties
Increase, lease, re-lease (in both
Senses); and immersion, conversion—of inert
Mass, that is, into energies to combat confusion.
Let rhyme be my conclusion.

Night Ride

The lamps are on: terrestrial galaxies,
  Fixed stars and moving. How many lights,
How many lives there are, cramped in beside
  This swathe of roadway. And its sodium circuits
Have ousted the glimmer of a thousand hearths
  To the margins of estates whose windows
Blaze over pastoral parentheses. Scatterings
  Trace out the contours of heights unseen,
Drip pendants across their slopes.
  Too many of us are edging behind each other
With dipped beams down the shining wet.
  Our lights seem more beautiful than our lives
In the pulse and grip of this city with neither
  Time nor space in which to define
Itself, its style, as each one feels
  His way among the catseyes and glittering asterisks
And home on home reverberates our wheels.

Foxes' Moon

Night over England's interrupted pastoral,
  And moonlight on the frigid lattices
Of pylons. The shapes of dusk
  Take on an edge, refined
By a drying wind and foxes bring
  Flint hearts and sharpened senses to
This desolation of grisaille in which the dew
  Grows clearer, colder. Foxes go

In their ravenous quiet to where
  The last farm meets the first
Row from the approaching town: they nose
  The garbage of the yards, move through
The white displacement of a daily view
  Uninterrupted. Warm sleepers turn,
Catch the thin volpine bark between
  Dream on dream, then lose it
To the babbling undertow they swim. These
  Are the fox hours, cleansed
Of all the meanings we can use
  And so refuse them. Foxes glow,
Ghosts unacknowledged in the moonlight
  Of the suburb, and like ghosts they flow
Back, racing the coming red, the beams
  Of early cars, a world not theirs
Gleaming from kindled windows, asphalt, wires.

In December

Cattle are crowding the salt-lick.
The gruel of mud icily thickens.
On the farm-boy's Honda a sweat of fog drops.
They are logging the woodland, the sole standing crop.

The Rich

I like the rich—the way
they say: 'I'm not made of money':
their favourite pastoral
is to think they're not rich at all—
poorer, perhaps, than you or me,
for they have the imagination of that fall
into the pinched decency
we take for granted. Of course,
they do want to be wanted
by all the skivvies and scrapers
who neither inherited nor rose.
But are they daft or deft,
when they proclaim themselves
men of the left, as if prepared
at the first premonitory flush
of the red dawn
to go rushing onto the street
and, share by share,
add to the common conflagration
their scorned advantage?
They know that it can't happen
in Worthing or Wantage:
with so many safety valves
between themselves and scalding,
all they have to fear
is wives, children, breath and balding.
And at worst
there is always some sunny
Aegean prospect. I like the rich—
they so resemble the rest
of us, except for their money.

Images of Perfection

. . . What do we see
In the perfect thing? Is our seeing
Merely a measuring, a satisfaction
To be compared? How do we know at sight
And for what they are, these rarenesses
That are right? In yesterday's sky
Every variety of cloud accompanied earth,
Mares' tails riding past mountainous anvils,
While their shadows expunged our own:
It was pure display—all a sky could put on
In a single day, and yet remain sky.
I mean, you felt in the air the sway
Of sudden apocalypse, complete revelation:
But what it came to was a lingering
At the edge of time, a perfect neighbouring,
Until the twilight brought it consummation,
Seeping in violet through the entire scene.
Where was the meaning, then? Did Eden
Greet us ungated? Or was that marrying
Purely imaginary and, if it were,
What do we see in the perfect thing?

Rhymes

Perfect is the word I can never hear
  Without a sensation as of seeing—
As though a place should grow perfectly clear,
  The light on the look of it agreeing
To show—not all there is to be seen,
  But all you would wish to know
At a given time. Word and world rhyme
  As the penstrokes might if you drew
The spaciousness reaching down through a valley view,
  Gathering the lines into its distances
As if they were streams, as if they were eye-beams:
  Perfect, then, the eye's command in its riding,
Perfect the coping hand, the hillslopes
  Drawing it into such sight the sight would miss,
Guiding the glance the way perfection is.

Notes

HOW STILL THE HAWK

A difficult poem, compressed and intellectually strenuous. Lines 4–6 imply the conflict between moral and aesthetic judgements, and the conundrum which natural ferocity always presents to someone who attempts to judge of right and wrong. (Ted Hughes's HAWK ROOSTING seems more like a representation of evil, but even in Hughes the 'innocence' of the natural animal is implied.) This poem is even terser than that of Hughes, and the short lines enact hanging and suspense. The last five lines are puzzling: who is 'him'? Perhaps it is the passionless observer, at a distance (see lines 4–6), who tends to see the 'aesthetic' beauty of the creature and miss 'The shrivelled circle/Of magnetic fear'.

WINTER ENCOUNTERS

A statement of coherence within life, the interdependence not only of landscape, houses and elements, but also of the people in this setting. The verse itself—varied, flexible, bridging steadily from line to line—holds together. The poem, about meetings and pairings, is not likely to fall apart.

WHAT IT WAS LIKE and HOW IT HAPPENED

These poems light up each other, and can also be read alongside WINTER ENCOUNTERS or SWIMMING CHENANGO LAKE. In a way these poems amount to a religious statement (if you happen to know the poetry of Gerard Manley Hopkins, that may help). But from experience the poet makes art, not dogma—it is the opening up, not the closing out of possibility.

THE WEATHERCOCKS

Verses three, four and five are a weathercock's-eye view. The whole poem is a celebration of the patterned richness of the seen world on days of clarity and wind. Celebration with awe: light and colour and line are almost too fierce for the eye, will almost 'melt' and 'waken' even the weathercocks.

ON A MEXICAN STRAW CHRIST

A poet's version of a great theme of painters. Why the short lines?

SWIMMING CHENANGO LAKE

This poem needs to be worked on: give yourself a couple of hours at it. Taken steadily, sentence by sentence, it is coherent and lucid.

eccentric (line 8): not having the same centre.
construe (11 lines from the end): translate in fragments.
unscaping (last line but one): destroying the individual character of things (the word borrowed from Hopkins).
obsidian (last line but one): dark rock, like bottle-glass—here a careful metaphor for the dark glassy water, which almost seems hard even as it flows.

The man has a name, and a conventional identity. But these are more or less lost as he swims: he is simply a human being 'fronting' the cold element of water, which in winter would kill him but as yet 'grasps' him with 'a kind of mercy'. It is a fundamental relationship: it seems a bit like being freed, 'take hold/On water's meaning'. But probably only partly; only beginning to understand.

So man and water meet, the man very vulnerable to cold and death, the element truly indifferent, but *seeming* to have character. (In some philosophies, the water would itself be part of God.)

But man and water are also in a scene, a picture. The first half of the poem is about the 'consistency', the 'theme' of the water before the swimmer breaks it. The 'geometry', and the latent art of the scene, is also part of the *character* of the water, part of God as some might say, part of *reality*. And at the end of this extraordinarily poised and original poem, the ripples resume their indifferent endless character. The movement of the poem, incidentally, and its scrupulous and echoing vocabulary, mirror themselves the 'theme': 'a consistency, the grain of the pulsating flow'.

AGAINST EXTREMITY

A poem of the late 1960s, which was a time not only of civil and political disturbance in the West, but also of an intellectual cult of violence, neurosis, 'mind-bending' and suicide. The particular reference in line 7 is to Anne Sexton's poem SYLVIA'S DEATH, on the death of Sylvia Plath. The poise of the poem defies subversion. Without being so regular as to be sing-songy, the first four lines do work like music and do make bridges—between the internal rhymes and between the lines ('spanned/Sustained'). We progress from the 'given good' (where *good* is the word arrived at) to the next line where *good* is the start of a new phrase—tilting the weight forward. Explore the meanings of 'possession' and 'possessed' to value the wisdom and calm of the last line, with its discreet but firm final rhyme.

A SENSE OF DISTANCE

The vividness of recollection of an American scene, and the vividness of introspection back home in England, are fused in the poet's mind and *with* the mind itself. Far from a door being shut, the door of the mind is opened on to limitlessness. This bringing together of disparate experience is Hopkins's inscape, or a mystic's vision; even Tomlinson allows himself an unusually grand flourish (think of the associations of 'kingdoms')—but he tempers it with a characteristically cautious title.

THE CHANCES OF RHYME

Sturm-und-Drang: 'Storm and Stress'—a literary phrase for upset and disturbance.

Crewe and *Mow Cop*: bleak places near the poet's birthplace.

Take care with the words *fortuitous* (it does *not* mean *fortunate*!), *vigilance*, and *circumstance*—the last largely explained for us in the poem.

This is a witty poem and a technical showpiece (most of the rhyme is in fact internal); but also a philosophy of poetry: 'conversion . . ., into energies to combat confusion.' To make bridges, too: in many ways this poem is an expansion of AGAINST EXTREMITY.

NIGHT RIDE

The modern road has been cut smoothly and harshly into the city, like the 'swathe' of a scythe in a field; and the families who lived where the road has gone have been moved to estates on the edge of landscape which is like enclosing brackets. The city has lost its self-knowledge, its character, and the only direction it seems to have now is in the sick beauty of the road-lights.

FOXES' MOON

interrupted pastoral: here, rural scene repeatedly broken by built-up areas.

grisaille: grey colourless painting.

volpine: fox's.

The fact that foxes do invade our towns and suburbs at night is linked quietly, gently, with the fact that in our dreams come unacceptable ideas—aspects of ourselves which remain 'ghosts unacknowledged'. But perhaps the 'meanings' we cannot 'use' are also those we cannot 'refuse'. And perhaps when we have *used* meanings we throw them aside as *refuse* or 'garbage'—to be nosed at night by foxes.

IN DECEMBER

Another painterly poem. Listen to the vowel-sounds too.

THE RICH

Tomlinson is good at sardonic and almost frivolous poems when he feels like it. And this one, it seems to me, needed writing. It should leave the reader winded from a sharp elbow-jab, just when he thought he was comfortable. . . .

IMAGES OF PERFECTION and RHYMES

These are the central poems in a sequence of four which seem related in idea. The preceding poem, not included here, contains the phrase 'an image of perfection'—and what follows here starts like an afterthought or a remark at a tangent. As it turns out, we are taken to the centre of the poet's curiosity and preoccupation—a reaching towards absolutes behind the chance patterns of existence, and particularly behind *visual* patterns.

Thom Gunn

Thom Gunn was born in 1929. He became known as a poet while still an undergraduate at Cambridge; he continued his studies in California and has lived mainly in America since 1954.

In spite of a readiness to associate himself with mildly subversive fashions—leather-jacketed motorcyclists in the 1950s, hallucinogenic drugs in the 1960s—Gunn is in many respects an academic and intellectual poet. His writing is characteristic of the sensitive but uncertain late-twentieth-century thinker, as ready to criticize his own motives as anyone else's, specializing in intelligent puzzlement rather than brash solutions. Its achievement seems to me above all one of poise, perhaps associated with his skill in verse.

Most of Gunn's verse is either metrical or syllabic, and most of it uses rhyme. Somewhere in the background of most poetry is its origin in chant, but in few post-war poets does it sound so steadily as in Gunn. A poem, even on so modern and violent a subject as motorcycle gangs, is controlled and distanced by the patterning of verse: it takes on the sound of ritual or ceremony rather than journalistic anecdote, and the measured verse tends to moderate subjectivity, to depersonalize and generalize, which is what seventeenth- or eighteenth-century writers wanted and seems to have been what Gunn wanted in his earlier poems. This metrical verse is in eight- or ten-syllable iambic lines (with four or five stresses respectively): rhyme-schemes clinch the discipline, and the whole tone is rationalist.

Syllabic verse does not have regular stresses: the feeling is of relative informality and spontaneity, but a kind of quiet arbitrary control is exercised by the fact that every line has the same number of syllables. More recently Gunn has been ready to write free verse, neither metrical nor syllabic, running the associated risks of looseness and limpness, but gaining in subjectivity and apparent honesty. Perhaps he is now less interested in the mask of Poet.

Tamer and Hawk

I thought I was so tough,
But gentled at your hands
Cannot be quick enough
To fly for you and show
That when I go I go
At your commands.

Even in flight above
I am no longer free:
You seeled me with your love,
I am blind to other birds—
The habit of your words
Has hooded me.

As formerly, I wheel
I hover and I twist,
But only want the feel
In my possessive thought,
Of catcher and of caught
Upon your wrist.

You but half-civilize,
Taming me in this way.
Through having only eyes
For you I fear to lose,
I lose to keep, and choose
Tamer as prey.

On the Move

'Man, you gotta Go.'

The blue jay scuffling in the bushes follows
Some hidden purpose, and the gust of birds
That spurts across the field, the wheeling swallows,
Have nested in the trees and undergrowth.
Seeking their instinct, or their poise, or both,
One moves with an uncertain violence
Under the dust thrown by a baffled sense
Or the dull thunder of approximate words.

On motorcycles, up the road, they come:
Small, black, as flies hanging in heat, the Boys,
Until the distance throws them forth, their hum
Bulges to thunder held by calf and thigh.
In goggles, donned impersonality,
In gleaming jackets trophied with the dust,
They strap in doubt—by hiding it, robust—
And almost hear a meaning in their noise.

Exact conclusion of their hardiness
Has no shape yet, but from known whereabouts
They ride, direction where the tires press.
They scare a flight of birds across the field:
Much that is natural, to the will must yield.
Men manufacture both machine and soul,
And use what they imperfectly control
To dare a future from the taken routes.

It is a part solution, after all.
One is not necessarily discord
On earth; or damned because, half animal,
One lacks direct instinct, because one wakes
Afloat on movement that divides and breaks.
One joins the movement in a valueless world,
Choosing it, till, both hurler and the hurled,
One moves as well, always toward, toward.

A minute holds them, who have come to go:
The self-defined, astride the created will
They burst away; the towns they travel through
Are home for neither bird nor holiness,
For birds and saints complete their purposes.
At worst, one is in motion; and at best,
Reaching no absolute, in which to rest,
One is always nearer by not keeping still.

California

Jesus and His Mother

My only son, more God's than mine,
Stay in this garden ripe with pears.
The yielding of their substance wears
A modest and contented shine:
And when they weep with age, not brine
But lazy syrup are their tears.
'I am my own and not my own.'

He seemed much like another man,
That silent foreigner who trod
Outside my door with lily rod:
How could I know what I began
Meeting the eyes more furious than
The eyes of Joseph, those of God?
I was my own and not my own.

And who are these twelve labouring men?
I do not understand your words:
I taught you speech, we named the birds,
You marked their big migrations then
Like any child. So turn again
To silence from the place of crowds.
'I am my own and not my own.'

Why are you sullen when I speak?
Here are your tools, the saw and knife
And hammer on your bench. Your life
Is measured here in week and week
Planed as the furniture you make,
And I will teach you like a wife
To be my own and all my own.

Who like an arrogant wind blown
Where he may please, needs no content?
Yet I remember how you went
To speak with scholars in furred gown.
I hear an outcry in the town;
Who carries that dark instrument?
'One all his own and not his own.'

Treading the green and nimble sward,
I stare at a strange shadow thrown.
Are you the boy I bore alone,
No doctor near to cut the cord?
I cannot reach to call you Lord,
Answer me as my only son.
'I am my own and not my own.'

To Yvor Winters, 1955

I leave you in your garden.
In the yard
Behind it, run the airedales you have reared
With boxer's vigilance and poet's rigour:
Dog-generations you have trained the vigour
That few can breed to train and fewer still
Control with the deliberate human will.
And in the house there rest, piled shelf on shelf,
The accumulations that compose the self—
Poem and history: for if we use
Words to maintain the actions that we choose,
Our words, with slow defining influence,
Stay to mark out our chosen lineaments.

Continual temptation waits on each
To renounce his empire over thought and speech,
Till he submit his passive faculties
To evening, come where no resistance is;
The unmotivated sadness of the air
Filling the human with his own despair.

Where now lies power to hold the evening back?
Implicit in the grey is total black:
Denial of the discriminating brain
Brings the neurotic vision, and the vein
Of necromancy. All as relative
For mind as for the sense, we have to live
In a half-world, not ours nor history's,
And learn the false from half-true premisses.

But sitting in the dusk—though shapes combine,
Vague mass replacing edge and flickering line,
You keep both Rule and Energy in view,
Much power in each, most in the balanced two:
Ferocity existing in the fence
Built by an exercised intelligence.
Though night is always close, complete negation
Ready to drop on wisdom and emotion,
Night from the air or the carnivorous breath,
Still it is right to know the force of death,
And, as you do, persistent, tough in will,
Raise from the excellent the better still.

Considering the Snail

The snail pushes through a green
night, for the grass is heavy
with water and meets over
the bright path he makes, where rain
has darkened the earth's dark. He
moves in a wood of desire,

pale antlers barely stirring
as he hunts. I cannot tell
what power is at work, drenched there
with purpose, knowing nothing.
What is a snail's fury? All
I think is that if later

I parted the blades above
the tunnel and saw the thin
trail of broken white across
litter, I would never have
imagined the slow passion
to that deliberate progress.

'Blackie, the Electric Rembrandt'

We watch through the shop-front while
Blackie draws stars—an equal

concentration on his and
the youngster's faces. The hand

is steady and accurate;
but the boy does not see it

for his eyes follow the point
that touches (quick, dark movement!)

a virginal arm beneath
his rolled sleeve: he holds his breath.

. . . Now that it is finished, he
hands a few bills to Blackie

and leaves with a bandage on
his arm, under which gleam ten

stars, hanging in a blue thick
cluster. Now he is starlike.

The Annihilation of Nothing

Nothing remained: Nothing, the wanton name
That nightly I rehearsed till led away
To a dark sleep, or sleep that held one dream.

In this a huge contagious absence lay,
More space than space, over the cloud and slime,
Defined but by the encroachments of its sway.

Stripped to indifference at the turns of time,
Whose end I knew, I woke without desire,
And welcomed zero as a paradigm.

But now it breaks—images burst with fire
Into the quiet sphere where I have bided,
Showing the landscape holding yet entire:

The power that I envisaged, that presided
Ultimate in its abstract devastations,
Is merely change, the atoms it divided

Complete, in ignorance, new combinations.
Only an infinite finitude I see
In those peculiar lovely variations.

It is despair that nothing cannot be
Flares in the mind and leaves a smoky mark
Of dread.
Look upward. Neither firm nor free,

Purposeless matter hovers in the dark.

The Last Man I

He avoids the momentous rhythm
of the sea, one hill suffices him
who has the entire world to choose from.

He melts through the brown and green silence
inspecting his traps, is lost in dense
thicket, or appears among great stones.

He builds no watch tower. He lives like
the birds, self-contained they hop and peck;
he could conceal himself for a week;

and he learns like them to keep movement
on the undipped wing of the present.
But sometimes when he wakes, with the print

of stone in his side, a relentless
memory of monstrous battle is
keener than counsel of the senses.

He opens, then, a disused channel
to the onset of hatred, until
the final man walks the final hill

without thought or feeling, as before.
If he preserves himself in nature,
it is as a lived caricature

of the race he happens to survive.
He is clothed in dirt. He lacks motive.
He is wholly representative.

The Last Man II

At last, my shout is answered! Are you near,
Man whom I cannot see but can hear?

Here.

The canyon hides you well, which well defended.
Sir, tell me, is the long war ended?

Ended.

I passed no human on my trip, a slow one.
Is it your luck, down there, to know one?

No one.

What have I left, who stood among mankind,
When the firm base is undermined?

A mind.

Yet, with a vacant landscape as its mirror,
What can it choose, to ease the terror?

Error.

Is there no feeling, then, that I can trust,
In spite of what we have discussed?

Disgust.

Memoirs of the World

It has turned cold. I have been gathering wood,
Numb-fingered, hardly feeling what I touched,
Turning crisp leaves to pick up where I could
The damp sticks from beneath them. I have crouched
Piling them up to dry, all afternoon,
And have heard all afternoon, over and over,
Two falling notes—a sweet disconsolate tune,
As if the bird called, from its twiggy cover,
Nót now, nót now, nót now.

I dislodge sticks for kindling, one by one,
From brambles. Struck by shade, I stand and see
Half-blinding me, the cold red setting sun
Through the meshed branches of a leafless tree.
It calls old sunsets to my mind, one most
Which coloured, similarly, the white grey, blackened
Iron and slabbed concrete of a sentry post
With its cold orange. Let me live, one second,
Nót now, nót now, nót now.

Most poignant and most weakening, that recall.
Although I lived from day to day, too, there.
Yet the comparison makes me sensible
Of the diminishing warmth and light, which were,
Or seem to have been, diminished less than now.
The bird stops. Hardening in the single present,
I know, hearing wind rattle in a bough,
I have always harked thus after an incessant
Nót now, nót now, nót now.

Pierce Street

Nobody home. Long threads of sunlight slant
Past curtains, blind, and slat, through the warm room.
The beams are dazzling, but, random and scant,
Pierce where they end
                                        small areas of the gloom
On curve of chairleg or a green stalk's bend.

I start exploring. Beds and canvases
Are shapes in each room off the corridor,
Their colours muted, square thick presences
Rising between
                                        the ceiling and the floor,
A furniture inferred much more than seen.

Here in the seventh room my search is done.
A bluefly circles, irregular and faint.
And round the wall above me friezes run:
Fixed figures drawn
                                        in charcoal or in paint.
Out of night now the flesh-tint starts to dawn.

Some stand there as if muffled from the cold,
Some naked in it, the wind around a roof.
But armed, their holsters as if tipped with gold.
And twice life-size—
                                        in line, in groups, aloof,
They all stare down with large abstracted eyes.

A silent garrison, and always there,
They are the soldiers of the imagination
Produced by it to guard it everywhere.
Bodied within
                                        the limits of their station
As, also, I am bodied in my skin,

They vigilantly preserve as they prevent
And are the thing they guard, having some time stood
Where the painter reached to make them permanent.
The floorboards creak.
                                        The house smells of its wood.
Those who are transitory can move and speak.

Autobiography

The sniff of the real, that's
what I'd want to get
            how it felt
to sit on Parliament
Hill on a May evening
studying for exams   skinny
seventeen   dissatisfied
            yet sniffing such
a potent air, smell of
grass in heat from
the day's sun

I'd been walking through the damp
rich ways by the ponds
and now lay on the upper
grass with Lamartine's poems

life seemed all
loss, and what was more
I'd lost whatever it was
before I'd even had it

a green dry prospect
distant babble of children
and beyond, distinct at
the end of the glow
St Paul's like a stone thimble

longing so hard to make
inclusions that the longing
has become   in memory
an inclusion

The Roadmap

If I saw you liked that dull unhappy boy
and let you be, and did not react
to see you driving off together
to the country on Sundays
                                                it was
to make your position indefensible
and, that established,
must not my own lack of blame
survive, copious?
(How can you answer back? You were in the wrong.)

I teased a schoolmaster when I was twelve
until his accumulated rage
was out of proportion to the offence.
Thus, I reasoned, there could be no offence.
My emotions drew up a roadmap.

Now my mind catches up and looks back.

And wreckages of trust litter the route
each an offence against me.
I gaze back
                in hardened innocence.

Notes

TAMER AND HAWK

seeled: sewed up the eyelids (a technical term from hawking).

A crisp song-like love-poem in a roughly seventeenth-century manner. Much of its appeal is in the delay of a rhyme to the second line of each verse till the shortened last line: this holds the whole verse together and signs it off with an elegant casualness.

ON THE MOVE

Dry and formal iambic pentameters present a quasi-philosophical statement, but not really a difficult one, though it is possible to drape words such as 'existentialist' across its bare bones. The world which the motorcyclists know is without values or purpose—making a contrast with the instinctual life of birds. The motorcyclists exemplify both the wish to do violence to the puzzling natural world and the illusion that restless activity makes one more likely to arrive at significance: both are twentieth-century errors. Gunn himself sported the black leather jacket in the 1950s, but the phrasing 'strap in doubt' seems carefully chosen: the doubt will not be removed but will be fastened more tightly to the motorcyclist.

The whole poem may seem an example of the rationalist approach at its most humourless and misguided. Motorcycling fast and noisily is just *exciting*, like rock music or rock-climbing—it is a crude and lively pleasure which should shake off the leaden hand of intellectual diagnosis. The trouble with this common-sense view is that the motorcyclists themselves—at least those whom Gunn writes about—are inclined to claim profounder significance for their activity, wearing uniform and insignia, riding in packs, and muttering 'Man, you gotta Go.' The claim to significance is theirs (rock musicians and rock-climbers sometimes exhibit similar tendencies!) and invites Gunn's diagnosis.

JESUS AND HIS MOTHER

The poem may originate in a painting of Madonna and Child among pear trees. The 'garden ripe with pears' seems to symbolize enclosed domestic safety (as opposed to the terrible destiny of a man-god). In such a garden a man (and his mother) might live to peaceful old age (but Gunn's phrase 'lazy syrup' undercuts). The poem, like many Madonna and Child paintings, speaks for any mother: her instinct is to want to keep her son, to be 'like a wife' to him, not to give him to the world. But she must watch him take on his independence in the hazards of adulthood, in his marriage, in the claims of those he will in turn lead and care for—and whom he therefore *belongs to.*

TO YVOR WINTERS, 1955

Young poets such as Gunn went to Stanford University in California to study verse with Winters, much as young musicians study composition with senior composers. Winters was a remarkably independent, tough-minded poet and critic standing in direct opposition to the main current of the past 150 years—Romanticism—and indeed to many aspects of liberal and relativist philosophy. Gunn writes here in the late seventeenth-century Heroic Couplet form, which Winters himself would approve, paying tribute to Winters's toughness of discrimination in a growing moral greyness.

CONSIDERING THE SNAIL

Seven-syllable lines without rhyme or end-stopping: the voice moves across the lines, and the syllabic pattern is unobtrusive. Compare the 'purpose' of the snail to the 'purposes' of the birds in ON THE MOVE.

'BLACKIE, THE ELECTRIC REMBRANDT'

The quiet concentration of the tattooist and his customer is finely conveyed by syllabic rather than metrical verse, poised by the most discreet of couplet rhyme-schemes. Nothing is overdeveloped here—the contrasting 'quick, dark movement!', suspended within the calm breath-holding sentence, leads delicately to the suggestions of 'virginal' and eventually to the compassionate sympathy—rather shaming us out of irony or cynicism—of the last four words.

THE ANNIHILATION OF NOTHING

There is a European tradition of writing which studies blackness as an absolute, contrasting it with the 'greyness' of scepticism or relativism. (Similarly a belief in absolute evil may imply absolute goodness.) In this poem the poet has been seduced by the 'wanton' idea of Nothingness: he was at peace dreaming of vacuum or absence which could transcend the 'cloud and slime' (Yeats's phrase is 'mire and blood') of physical reality—rather as for centuries men have envisioned an end to the world or the universe. Later in the poem he is baffled by the *unendingness* of things. Atoms—'in ignorance'—without consciousness or direction make up new combinations. The ending of things is an unending succession of changes. Matter is 'purposeless', and we have seen that this is a key concept to Gunn.

The classical pentameter lines are folded in a rhyme-scheme leading always on into the next verse—change rather than ending—until the final clinching line breaks the pattern by sealing it.

THE LAST MAN I and II

The first two of six poems grouped together under the title MISANTHROPOS (which suggests a man turned against mankind). In the first poem we see a man beginning to live like the birds (see ON THE MOVE) in the present and without a 'watch tower' for the future. His memories of the human race are of its disaster. When he is joined, in the second poem, by another man, there is no delight, only the bitterest of echoes (an idea found in seventeenth-century poetry).

MEMOIRS OF THE WORLD

Poem six of MISANTHROPOS. The man living 'from day to day' yearns for an escape from 'the single present'—into memories, and possibly into a future.

PIERCE STREET

The frieze-figures found on the walls of an artist's house—where there are no flesh-and-blood people to give a welcome—turn out to be what the poet is looking for ('My search is done'). The last two verses are a lucid statement of some of the value of human works of art. The final line seems to make a contrast between living men and painted figures—or does it?

AUTOBIOGRAPHY

From *Parliament Hill* Fields, in North London, the dome of St Paul's can be seen, several miles away in the heart of the city.

Lamartine is a French Romantic poet often regarded as expressing adolescent moods of wistful emotion, self-pity and regret.

The adolescent feels he loses hold on life, when he longs to grip it all *together*. The adult remembers adolescence with warmth as a time when the hold on life was real. It is a psychological insight. The freer verse-form makes the poet more naked, unpretentious.

THE ROADMAP

The openness and apparent casualness of this poem (though it clearly expresses serious moral pain) is worth contrasting with the harder, patterned manner of the early poem TAMER AND HAWK which begins this selection. It is possible to see that to Gunn this change is an advance, and yet to wonder if the earlier poem isn't more attractive to the reader (it is a neater artistic commodity).

Ted Hughes

Ted Hughes was born in Yorkshire in 1930, and now lives in Devon. As an undergraduate at Cambridge he began to make a reputation as a poet, and for many years now he has been recognized as a major writer. He has written brilliantly for children and for the theatre, and in poetry he has broken the moulds of conventional form and conventional assumption. Not everyone likes what Hughes has been doing in the 1970s, but it is so striking, so forceful, and written with such verbal mastery that perhaps everyone should know of it.

Hughes's early books, THE HAWK IN THE RAIN and LUPERCAL, used relatively traditional verse-forms—usually in four-line paragraphs, often with discreet half-rhymes—in making vivid word-pictures, quite easy to grasp. Many of these poems quickly found their way into schoolrooms, and to young people growing up in the 1960s they showed the quite unarchaic vitality of the English language, particularly its rougher, more Scandinavian elements: the monosyllabic words of concrete experience, heavy with consonantal clatter. Not that the diction stuck out on its own: these early Hughes poems were hot with the particular life of their subject-matter, represented in this selection by the 'sharp hot stink' of the thought-fox, the 'stampeding' wind, the jaguar 'hurrying enraged', 'the ammoniac reek' of the bull Moses, the pigs 'like ovens' and the hawk 'tearing off heads'. Sheer fierceness, it often seemed; but *real* fierceness, and created with the exactness and judgement of knowledge. Hughes, who has lived much of his life on farms, seems *inside* the natural world in a degree that makes other writers—even D. H. Lawrence, whose animal-poems showed the young Hughes the way in—appear like cool observers.

WODWO, Hughes's third collection, seemed to move away

from paragraphed verse and safely rounded-off views into a more and more uncertain and alarming world (such as that of A WIND FLASHES THE GRASS). Writing of Hughes for the first edition of this anthology, I suggested that he might be 'trying to achieve a modern re-statement of natural evil'. A few years later CROW appeared—wholly original, harsh, grotesque; and I would now say that Hughes had always been attempting a knowledge of natural *life*, the sheer survival-force, which might appear evil simply because it could hardly be seen as good. For Lawrence, for Christian writers such as Hopkins (whom Hughes also admires), for John Keats or William Wordsworth, and perhaps for Charles Tomlinson in this book, to encounter the essential life-force is to encounter goodness and meaning. For Hughes it is to encounter Crow. Many readers resist Crow because he is humanoid, thinking (or trying to) and articulate (more or less). They should perhaps return through Crow to the hawk roosting at the top of the wood (page 91) or simply to the fox 'coming about its own business' (page 85); and then, away from all personality, to the violence of the wind (page 86). Some critics acclaimed CROW as relevant to a world of concentration-camps and political prisoners (as if such inhumanity were new to the twentieth century). Well, it isn't *irrelevant* to such a world, but it is just as relevant to Stone Age man or the fears of Renaissance man, who exulted in magnificent aspiration but saw how it might prove—without God *would* prove—the carking of Crow.

We mustn't simplify or digress, however: CROW, and Hughes's poetry in general, will be of little value for the student who wants to translate it into crisp index-card philosophy: 'Hughes believes the world is meaningless.' What Hughes believes is, since he is not a philosopher or preacher, of as little importance to us as what Rembrandt or Shakespeare believed: what he offers us is not his belief but his attempt to see and know reality; or, rather, his attempt to make *poems* which deal in reality. Philosophy, morality: they are the reader's affair. And of course the reader may feel that

CROW doesn't get reality right at all; but its challenge has to be answered.

Approach CROW, then, through Hughes's other work—including such gentle and compassionate work as the book which followed it, SEASON SONGS (a marvellous tripwire for the index-card student who is inclined to say 'Hughes believes life is all grim'). Another approach which is important is through other art—through, say, the writings of Samuel Beckett, or a primitive phallic sculpture: they may suggest moralities or philosophies, but they are what they *are*: art is itself Crowing, as much a part of the life-force as anything. (What, by the way, might Shakespeare's HAMLET 'mean'?)

Or what might Hughes's next main creation after CROW, GAUDETE, 'mean'? It is a strange verse-novel (originating, we are told, in an idea for a film script) set in realistic Yorkshire countryside with realistic people, but telling a story of supernatural farce (a demon possesses the body of the parson, who then seduces every woman around). There is a collection of poetic fragments at the end, but the main narration does not divide itself up into separate 'poems' and to represent it in extract is hard; the pages I have chosen do at least demonstrate the fluent force of Hughes's descriptive writing and perhaps sum up themes discovered in the earlier poems. Lumb, the possessed parson, here seems not so far from Hughes or the man in Hughes's story THE RAIN HORSE or, really, from Crow himself:

'He is clearly aware of himself, on the hill in clear light, from the eye of a soaring, reconnoitring and downsliding far crow.'

The Thought-Fox

I imagine this midnight moment's forest:
Something else is alive
Beside the clock's loneliness
And this blank page where my fingers move.

Through the window I see no star:
Something more near
Though deeper within darkness
Is entering the loneliness:

Cold, delicately as the dark snow,
A fox's nose touches twig, leaf;
Two eyes serve a movement, that now
And again now, and now, and now

Sets neat prints into the snow
Between trees, and warily a lame
Shadow lags by stump and in hollow
Of a body that is bold to come

Across clearings, an eye,
A widening deepening greenness,
Brilliantly, concentratedly,
Coming about its own business

Till, with a sudden sharp hot stink of fox
It enters the dark hole of the head.
The window is starless still; the clock ticks,
The page is printed.

Wind

This house has been far out at sea all night,
The woods crashing through darkness, the booming hills,
Wind stampeding the fields under the window
Floundering black astride and blinding wet

Till day rose; then under an orange sky
The hills had new places, and wind wielded
Blade-light, luminous black and emerald,
Flexing like the lens of a mad eye.

At noon I scaled along the house-side as far as
The coal-house door. I dared once to look up—
Through the brunt wind that dented the balls of my eyes
The tent of the hills drummed and strained its guyrope,

The fields quivering, the skyline a grimace,
At any second to bang and vanish with a flap:
The wind flung a magpie away and a black-
Back gull bent like an iron bar slowly. The house

Rang like some fine green goblet in the note
That any second would shatter it. Now deep
In chairs, in front of the great fire, we grip
Our hearts and cannot entertain book, thought,

Or each other. We watch the fire blazing,
And feel the roots of the house move, but sit on,
Seeing the window tremble to come in,
Hearing the stones cry out under the horizons.

The Jaguar

The apes yawn and adore their fleas in the sun.
The parrots shriek as if they were on fire, or strut
Like cheap tarts to attract the stroller with the nut.
Fatigued with indolence, tiger and lion

Lie still as the sun. The boa-constrictor's coil
Is a fossil. Cage after cage seems empty, or
Stinks of sleepers from the breathing straw.
It might be painted on a nursery wall.

But who runs like the rest past these arrives
At a cage where the crowd stands, stares, mesmerized,
As a child at a dream, at a jaguar hurrying enraged
Through prison darkness after the drills of his eyes

On a short fierce fuse. Not in boredom—
The eye satisfied to be blind in fire,
By the bang of blood in the brain deaf the ear—
He spins from the bars, but there's no cage to him

More than to the visionary his cell:
His stride is wildernesses of freedom:
The world rolls under the long thrust of his heel.
Over the cage floor the horizons come.

The Bull Moses

A hoist up and I could lean over
The upper edge of the high half-door,
My left foot ledged on the hinge, and look in at the
byre's
Blaze of darkness: a sudden shut-eyed look
Backward into the head.
Blackness is depth
Beyond star. But the warm weight of his breathing,
The ammoniac reek of his litter, the hotly-tongued
Mash of his cud, steamed against me.
Then, slowly, as onto the mind's eye—
The brow like masonry, the deep-keeled neck:
Something come up there onto the brink of the gulf,
Hadn't heard of the world, too deep in itself to be
called to,
Stood in sleep. He would swing his muzzle at a fly
But the square of sky where I hung, shouting, waving,
Was nothing to him; nothing of our light
Found any reflection in him.
Each dusk the farmer led him
Down to the pond to drink and smell the air,

And he took no pace but the farmer
Led him to take it, as if he knew nothing
Of the ages and continents of his fathers,
Shut, while he wombed, to a dark shed
And steps between his door and the duckpond;
The weight of the sun and the moon and the world
hammered
To a ring of brass through his nostrils.
He would raise

His streaming muzzle and look out over the meadows,
But the grasses whispered nothing awake, the fetch
Of the distance drew nothing to momentum
In the locked black of his powers. He came strolling
gently back,
Paused neither toward the pig-pens on his right,
Nor toward the cow-byres on his left: something
Deliberate in his leisure, some beheld future
Founding in his quiet.
I kept the door wide,
Closed it after him and pushed the bolt.

View of a Pig

The pig lay on a barrow dead.
It weighed, they said, as much as three men.
Its eyes closed, pink white eyelashes.
Its trotters stuck straight out.

Such weight and thick pink bulk
Set in death seemed not just dead.
It was less than lifeless, further off.
It was like a sack of wheat.

I thumped it without feeling remorse.
One feels guilty insulting the dead,
Walking on graves. But this pig
Did not seem able to accuse.

It was too dead. Just so much
A poundage of lard and pork.
Its last dignity had entirely gone.
It was not a figure of fun.

Too dead now to pity.
To remember its life, din, stronghold
Of earthly pleasure as it had been,
Seemed a false effort, and off the point.

Too deadly factual. Its weight
Oppressed me—how could it be moved?
And the trouble of cutting it up!
The gash in its throat was shocking, but not pathetic.

Once I ran at a fair in the noise
To catch a greased piglet
That was faster and nimbler than a cat,
Its squeal was the rending of metal.

Pigs must have hot blood, they feel like ovens.
Their bite is worse than a horse's—
They chop a half-moon clean out.
They eat cinders, dead cats.

Distinctions and admirations such
As this one was long finished with.
I stared at it a long time. They were going to scald it,
Scald it and scour it like a doorstep.

Hawk Roosting

I sit in the top of the wood, my eyes closed.
Inaction, no falsifying dream
Between my hooked head and hooked feet:
Or in sleep rehearse perfect kills and eat.

The convenience of the high trees!
The air's buoyancy and the sun's ray
Are of advantage to me;
And the earth's face upward for my inspection.

My feet are locked upon the rough bark.
It took the whole of Creation
To produce my foot, my each feather:
Now I hold Creation in my foot

Or fly up, and revolve it all slowly—
I kill where I please because it is all mine.
There is no sophistry in my body:
My manners are tearing off heads—

The allotment of death.
For the one path of my flight is direct
Through the bones of the living.
No arguments assert my right:

The sun is behind me.
Nothing has changed since I began.
My eye has permitted no change.
I am going to keep things like this.

Full Moon and Little Frieda

A cool small evening shrunk to a dog bark and the
clank of a bucket—

And you listening.
A spider's web, tense for the dew's touch.
A pail lifted, still and brimming—mirror
To tempt a first star to a tremor.

Cows are going home in the lane there, looping the
hedges with their warm wreaths of breath—
A dark river of blood, many boulders,
Balancing unspilled milk.

'Moon!' you cry suddenly, 'Moon! Moon!'

The moon has stepped back like an artist gazing
amazed at a work
That points at him amazed.

A Wind Flashes the Grass

Leaves pour blackly across.
We cling to the earth, with glistening eyes, pierced
afresh by the tree's cry.

And the incomprehensible cry
From the boughs, in the wind
Sets us listening for below words,
Meanings that will not part from the rock.

The trees thunder in unison, on a gloomy afternoon,
And the ploughman grows anxious, his tractor becomes
terrible,
As his memory litters downwind
And the shadows of his bones toss darkly on the air.

The trees suddenly storm to a stop, in a hush,
Against the sky, where the field ends,
And crowd there, shuddering
And wary, like horses bewildered by lightning.

The stirring of their twigs against the dark, travelling
sky
Is the oracle of the earth.

They too are afraid they too are momentary
Streams rivers of shadow.

Crow's Theology

Crow realized God loved him—
Otherwise, he would have dropped dead.
So that was proved.
Crow reclined, marvelling, on his heart-beat.

And he realized that God spoke Crow—
Just existing was His revelation.

But what
Loved the stones and spoke stone?
They seemed to exist too.
And what spoke that strange silence
After his clamour of caws faded?

And what loved the shot-pellets
That dribbled from those strung-up mummifying
   crows?
What spoke the silence of lead?

Crow realized there were two Gods—

One of them much bigger than the other
Loving his enemies
And having all the weapons.

Crow on the Beach

Hearing shingle explode, seeing it skip,
Crow sucked his tongue.
Seeing sea-grey mash a mountain of itself
Crow tightened his goose-pimples.
Feeling spray from the sea's root nothinged on his crest
Crow's toes gripped the wet pebbles.
When the smell of the whale's den, the gulfing of the
crab's last prayer,
Gimletted in his nostril
He grasped he was on earth.
He knew he grasped
Something fleeting
Of the sea's ogreish outcry and convulsion.
He knew he was the wrong listener unwanted
To understand or help—

His utmost gaping of brain in his tiny skull
Was just enough to wonder, about the sea,

What could be hurting so much?

Crow's Vanity

Looking close in the evil mirror Crow saw
Mistings of civilizations   towers   gardens
Battles he wiped the glass   but there came

Mistings of skyscrapers   webs of cities
Steaming the glass he wiped it   there came

Spread of swampferns fronded on the mistings
A trickling spider   he wiped the glass   he peered

For a glimpse of the usual grinning face

But it was no good he was breathing too heavy
And too hot   and space was too cold

And here came the misty ballerinas
The burning gulfs   the hanging gardens   it was eerie

Crow's Playmates

Lonely Crow created the gods for playmates—
But the mountain god tore free

And Crow fell back from the wall-face of mountains
By which he was so much lessened.

The river-god subtracted the rivers
From his living liquids.

God after god—and each tore from him
Its lodging place and its power.

Crow straggled, limply bedraggled his remnant.
He was his own leftover, the spat-out scrag.

He was what his brain could make nothing of.

So the least, least-living object extant
Wandered over his deathless greatness

Lonelier than ever.

Crow's Song of Himself

When God hammered Crow
He made gold
When God roasted Crow in the sun
He made diamond
When God crushed Crow under weights
He made alcohol
When God tore Crow to pieces
He made money
When God blew Crow up
He made day
When God hung Crow on a tree
He made fruit
When God buried Crow in the earth
He made man
When God tried to chop Crow in two
He made woman
When God said: 'You win, Crow,'
He made the Redeemer.

When God went off in despair
Crow stropped his beak and started in on the two thieves.

The River in March

Now the river is rich, but her voice is low.
It is her Mighty Majesty the sea
Travelling among the villages incognito.

Now the river is poor. No song, just a thin mad whisper.
The winter floods have ruined her.
She squats between draggled banks, fingering her rags and rubbish.

And now the river is rich. A deep choir.
It is the lofty clouds, that work in heaven,
Going on their holiday to the sea.

The river is poor again. All her bones are showing.
Through a dry wig of bleached flotsam she peers up ashamed
From her slum of sticks.

Now the river is rich, collecting shawls and minerals.
Rain brought fatness, but she takes ninety-nine percent
Leaving the fields just one percent to survive on.

And now she is poor. Now she is East wind sick.
She huddles in holes and corners. The brassy sun gives her a headache.
She has lost all her fish. And she shivers.

But now once more she is rich. She is viewing her lands.
A hoard of king-cups spills from her folds, it blazes,
it cannot be hidden.
A salmon, a sow of solid silver,

Bulges to glimpse it.

Spring Nature Notes

The sun lies mild and still on the yard stones.

The clue is a solitary daffodil—the first.

And the whole air struggling in soft excitements
Like a woman hurrying into her silks.
Birds everywhere zipping and unzipping
Changing their minds, in soft excitements,
Warming their wings and trying their voices.

The trees still spindle bare.

Beyond them, from the warmed blue hills
An exhilaration swirls upward, like a huge fish.

As under a waterfall, in the bustling pool.

Over the whole land
Spring thunders down in brilliant silence.

from Gaudete

Lumb
Is looking at the land.
This is the unalterably strange earth.
He is looking at the sky. He looks down at the soil,
between the grass.
He looks at the trees
Which clamber in a tangle up the slope towards him,
from the river, out of the swell of land beyond.

He listens to all this, and listens into the emptiness
beyond it
And the emptiness within it.
And the soft hollow air noises among it.

It feels very like safety. If the trees were trees only, wood only, were simple roots and boles and boughs and leaves, and that only, as the stones should be stones. If the stones were simple stones. This would be safe. All this would be safety.

But he knows everything he looks at,
Even the substance of his fingers, and the near-wall of
his skin,
He knows it is vibrant with peril, like a blurred speed-
vibration.
He knows the blood in his veins
Is like heated petrol, as if it were stirring closer and
closer to explosion,
As if his whole body were a hot engine, growing hotter
Connected to the world, which is out of control,
And to the grass under his feet, the trees whose
shadows reach for him.

He breathes deeply and strongly to confirm his solidity,
To cool his outline and his solidity
To fill his strength
Against the power that beats up against him, beating at
the soles of his feet,

Beating through his thoughts
And the obscure convulsions and blunderings of a
music that lurches through him
With brightenings and darkenings, and rendings and
caressings,
With tiny crowded farness and near sudden hugeness
And hot twisting roughness, and vast cantileverings of
star-balance.

He looks out across the quilt and embroidery of the
landscape,
The hazings of distance, and the watery horizons
folded like fingers,
And tries to imagine simple freedom—
His possible freedoms, his other lives, hypothetical and
foregone, his lost freedoms.
As each person carries the whole world, like a halo,
Albeit a dim and mostly provisional world, but with a
brightly focused centre, under the sun,
Considering their millions
All mutually exclusive, all conjunct and co-extensive,
He sees in among them,
In among all the tiny millions of worlds of this world
Millions of yet other, alternative worlds, uninhabited,
unnoticed, still empty,
Each open at every point to every other and yet distinct,

Each waiting for him to escape into it, to explore it and
possess it,
Each with a bed at the centre. A name. A pair of shoes.
And a door.
And surrounded by still-empty, never-used limitless
freedom.
He yields to his favourite meditation.
Forlorn, desperate meditation.

Between the root in immovable earth
And the coming and going leaf
Stands the tree
Of what he cannot alter.
As his heart surges after his reverie, with lofty cries and
lifting wingbeats
Suddenly he comes against the old trees
And feels the branches in his throat, and the leaves at
his lips.
He sees the grass
And feels the wind pulse over his skin.
He feels the hill he stands on, hunched, swelling,
Piling through him, complete and permanent with stone,
Filling his skull, squeezing his thoughts out from his eyes
To fritter away across surfaces.

Till the one presence of world crushes him from himself,
and sits on him like an iron crown on a stone pillar,
Studded with baleful stones,
As if he were a child king, hoisted on to a granite throne,
surrounded by eyes of sharpened metal.
For a half hour he stands, alert
Imprisoned in the globe's stoniness
And the thin skin, the thin painting of mother-soil,
And the hair-fine umbilicus of life in the stalk of grass.

His life returns as a fly. It lands on his eyelid and trickles
down to his mouth-corner.
He moves to free himself.
Some animal is pushing noisily below in the wood.
A squirrel flees up through a beech, like a lashing rocket,
and rips into the outermost leaf-net with a crash.
Voices recede, snatch back their words and meanings,
Become bramble stem, leaf hollows, reticulation of
twigs.
He is clearly aware of himself, on the hill in clear light,
from the eye of a soaring, reconnoitring and
downsliding far crow.
He prays
To be guided. He feels his prayer claw at the air, as at
glass
Like a beetle in a bottle.

Notes

THE THOUGHT-FOX

A poem about writing a poem: first it is sensed, but not there; gradually it emerges, suddenly it happens. The fox, then, is a symbol, or an extended metaphor; but it is itself created with great precision and immediacy.

There is rhyme but rarely exact rhyme; four-line groupings but running on from one to another—a sense of control without certainty, and of exploration rather than arrival. It is a puzzled poem, trying to come to terms with a mystery.

WIND

The natural universe can be terrifying, breaking all routine and security. The violence of the wind is superbly presented in the verbs and participles of straining motion, the brutal surrealism of 'Flexing like the lens of a mad eye', and the images of tension in the later verses.

the brunt wind: the full force of the wind.

THE JAGUAR

This is as good a place as any to study the early Hughes's mastery of conventional poetic form: rhyme and half-rhyme, the five-stress line, and verse-movement. The mid-line full-stops serve real purpose, first by bringing the verse, appropriately, almost to a standstill (stanza two) and secondly, by highlighting the sharp hissing onomatopeia of 'a short fierce fuse' (stanza four). The last three lines give us the huge ranging strides of the jaguar: each line is a new horizon. As for the imagery, note how it can be doubly appropriate: 'as if they were on fire' and 'Like cheap tarts' describe not only the noise and movement of the parrots, but also their colour; the comparison of the boa-constrictor's coil to a fossil shows us not only its stillness but also its texture. In admiring all this we can also note how attracted Hughes is by this natural ferocity.

THE BULL MOSES

It's like a visit to a god—the bull is almost too lethargic to stir, seeming scarcely alive in our world at all, but in fact both hugely alive and also a giver of life. The mystery of the life-force itself is met: 'Something come up there onto the brink of the gulf,/Hadn't heard of the world, too deep in itself to be called to,/Stood in sleep.'

VIEW OF A PIG

That the greased piglet at the fair and the thumpable carcass at the market should be the same thing is incredible. The poem deals mainly with the great dead weight of the carcass: note the clipped, heavy sentences (the poem has an extraordinary number of full-stops to lines) and phrases which carry in their sound the suggestion of their subject: 'stuck straight out . . .' 'thick pink bulk'.

The bewilderment is not that of violent emotion, but of absence of emotion. A dead pig ought to be either tragic, being dead, or comic, being a pig. It is neither.

The first sentence of the last verse means: 'I have just listed distinctions (of pigs) and admirations (which I feel) of a sort which this particular pig would have nothing further to do with.' The poet has saved his most forceful image for the end: what could be flatter, heavier, deader than a doorstep?

HAWK ROOSTING

The hawk is not, in Hughes, a *metaphor* for a fanatic in power or a hostile Creator. It is itself fanatic and hostile: that is part of being a hawk. Hughes's poem is written not to illuminate for us human tyranny, but to illuminate the natural world (of which human tyranny is, to be sure, a part).

The diction is prissy, clipped, and the sentences get shorter and shorter as the fanaticism clamps in, till each of the last few lines is its own snapped, grudging statement.

FULL MOON AND LITTLE FRIEDA

A moment caught, but not interpreted: a poem seeming to occur rather than be composed. The technical dexterity of the earlier Hughes's stanzaic verse would not be right here at all. It is the finest of imagist poems—most gentle and sensitive, but with latent heat and power ('A dark river of blood'). And could that be the voice of Crow hardening in the last two lines? Don't we step back ourselves, a little chilled, at the end?

Minor poems like this are not written by minor poets.

A WIND FLASHES THE GRASS

Hughes's earlier poems, such as WIND, *hinted* at terror, but ordered it within stanzaic verse, rhyme, and even wit. In the volume WODWO, from which this poem is taken, terror and strangeness are allowed more dominance, and find a freer (but still incantatory-rhythmical, still controlled) form. Notice that the ploughman's 'memory' litters like leaves on the wind: it is not just the shadow of death but the questionableness of the past and of all experience which terrify and make us 'cling to the earth'. And even the trees are mortal and afraid.

FIVE POEMS FROM CROW

CROW is a sequence of sixty poems; the five printed here need reading together, just as the whole sequence really needs reading as a whole. Each poem, however, is a complete epigram. The poems ask to be spoken aloud to an audience: a series of comments on existence (not particularly *human* existence, of course), survival, self-interest, suffering, and the inadequacy of conventional myth-explanations. Each poem has its fresh stance, image or story.

Why 'Crow'? The black birds—raven, crow, rook—have traditionally dark and sinister associations: harsh-voiced portents. But *to* crow is to exult—callously and crudely, but with energy—to waken the world, or to delight in another's downfall. Now that Hughes has invented Crow it is hard to think of him as anything else: he has the apparent inevitability of a really bold and successful artistic creation.

THE RIVER IN MARCH

This poem and the one that follows are from Hughes's most attractive and delightful collection, SEASON SONGS. He has a young people's audience first in mind; but the liveliness and energy of his imagination should be shared with all readers.

From GAUDETE

Lumb is a parson, inhabited by demons. How much that matters, in this extract, is debatable: it seems to me that Hughes is talking about being alive and feeling and knowing it—as in A WIND FLASHES THE GRASS. Lumb's demons here only make him more intensely human. The passage as a whole is authentic Hughes.

Sylvia Plath

Sylvia Plath was born in Boston, Massachusetts, in 1932. After an American education she came to England to do further study at Cambridge; there she met and married Ted Hughes. She took her own life in 1963 after surviving a number of previous depressions.

After her death several volumes of Sylvia Plath's poetry appeared and were much admired. The sharpness of her painful imagination, linked to a most accomplished verse technique, make her work quite distinctive.

Beyond agreeing on this, however, readers differ in their reactions to the poetry, depending rather on their personal sense of the world or of art. Charles Tomlinson's poem AGAINST EXTREMITY (page 45) expresses his antipathy for a cult of dislocation, sickness and defeat. Other critics find the vision of Sylvia Plath illuminating, like, perhaps, expressionist painting (Van Gogh's cornfields, Munch's SCREAM): the horror of alienation (where small fish 'glitter like eyes') or inverted vision (where trees are 'like black holes cut out of the landscape') are part of real experience, just as health and delight are part of it. (Some readers may find Jean-Paul Sartre's novel NAUSEA relevant.)

In Tomlinson experience knits *together*—movement and colour and light gather in pattern and harmony. In Plath discontinuity leads to disproportion—things do not stay in their places, tulips open 'like the mouth of some great African cat', the moon 'drags the sea after it like a dark crime', and the 'tricks of radiance' such as that described in BLACK ROOK IN RAINY WEATHER are 'spasmodic' and 'random' and assault the poet ('set the sight on fire in my eye', 'seize my senses, haul my eyelids up'). Unlike Hughes—whose poetry though harsh and violent tends to imply a single energy of nature, reaching towards unity and identity—Plath is hypnotized by fragments of experience. There is no 'overview': no escape, really, from the private strained consciousness. To be 'idiot' is to be too solely oneself; as Hopkins put it, 'My taste was me: self-yeast of spirit a dull dough sours'. All this Plath knows and tells, but cannot transcend.

Except, of course, to the extent that she makes art. To make a poem, finely controlled and shaped, is to create outside oneself. An achieved poem becomes other people's: they can walk round it like a sculpture, there is no umbilical cord connecting it to the poet's life-blood, it has its own independent life. These poems are ours now.

Black Rook in Rainy Weather

On the stiff twig up there
Hunches a wet black rook
Arranging and rearranging its feathers in the rain.
I do not expect miracle
Or an accident

To set the sight on fire
In my eye, nor seek
Any more in the desultory weather some design,
But let spotted leaves fall as they fall,
Without ceremony, or portent.

Although, I admit, I desire,
Occasionally, some backtalk
From the mute sky, I can't honestly complain:
A certain minor light may still
Leap incandescent

Out of kitchen table or chair
As if a celestial burning took
Possession of the most obtuse objects now and then—
Thus hallowing an interval
Otherwise inconsequent

By bestowing largesse, honour,
One might say love. At any rate, I now walk
Wary (for it could happen
Even in this dull, ruinous landscape); sceptical,
Yet politic; ignorant

Of whatever angel may choose to flare
Suddenly at my elbow. I only know that a rook
Ordering its black feathers can so shine
As to seize my senses, haul
My eyelids up, and grant

A brief respite from fear
Of total neutrality. With luck,
Trekking stubborn through this season
Of fatigue, I shall
Patch together a content

Of sorts. Miracles occur,
If you care to call those spasmodic
Tricks of radiance miracles. The wait's begun again,
The long wait for the angel,
For that rare, random descent.

Medallion

By the gate with star and moon
Worked into the peeled orange wood
The bronze snake lay in the sun

Inert as a shoelace; dead
But pliable still, his jaw
Unhinged and his grin crooked,

Tongue a rose-coloured arrow.
Over my hand I hung him.
His little vermilion eye

Ignited with a glassed flame
As I turned him in the light;
When I split a rock one time

The garnet bits burned like that.
Dust dulled his back to ochre
The way sun ruins a trout.

Yet his belly kept its fire
Going under the chainmail,
The old jewels smouldering there

In each opaque belly-scale:
Sunset looked at through milk glass.
And I saw white maggots coil

Thin as pins in the dark bruise
Where his innards bulged as if
He were digesting a mouse.

Knifelike, he was chaste enough,
Pure death's-metal. The yardman's
Flung brick perfected his laugh.

Crossing the Water

Black lake, black boat, two black, cut-paper people.
Where do the black trees go that drink here?
Their shadows must cover Canada.

A little light is filtering from the water flowers.
Their leaves do not wish us to hurry:
They are round and flat and full of dark advice.

Cold worlds shake from the oar.
The spirit of blackness is in us, it is in the fishes.
A snag is lifting a valedictory, pale hand;

Stars open among the lilies.
Are you not blinded by such expressionless sirens?
This is the silence of astounded souls.

Blackberrying

Nobody in the lane, and nothing, nothing but
blackberries,
Blackberries on either side, though on the right mainly,
A blackberry alley, going down in hooks, and a sea
Somewhere at the end of it, heaving. Blackberries
Big as the ball of my thumb, and dumb as eyes
Ebon in the hedges, fat
With blue-red juices. These they squander on my
fingers.

I had not asked for such a blood sisterhood; they must
love me.
They accommodate themselves to my milkbottle,
flattening their sides.

Overhead go the choughs in black, cacophonous flocks—
Bits of burnt paper wheeling in a blown sky.
Theirs is the only voice, protesting, protesting.
I do not think the sea will appear at all.
The high, green meadows are glowing, as if lit from
within.
I come to one bush of berries so ripe it is a bush of
flies,
Hanging their bluegreen bellies and their wing
panes in a Chinese screen.
The honey-feast of the berries has stunned them;
they believe in heaven.
One more hook, and the berries and bushes end.

The only thing to come now is the sea.
From between two hills a sudden wind funnels at me,
Slapping its phantom laundry in my face.
These hills are too green and sweet to have tasted salt.
I follow the sheep path between them. A last hook
brings me
To the hills' northern face, and the face is orange rock
That looks out on nothing, nothing but a great space
Of white and pewter lights, and a din like silversmiths
Beating and beating at an intractable metal.

Private Ground

First frost, and I walk among the rose-fruit, the marble toes
Of the Greek beauties you brought
Off Europe's relic heap
To sweeten your neck of the New York woods.
Soon each white lady will be boarded up
Against the cracking climate.

All morning, with smoking breath, the handyman
Has been draining the goldfish ponds.
They collapse like lungs, the escaped water
Threading back, filament by filament, to the pure
Platonic table where it lives. The baby carp
Litter the mud like orangepeel.

Eleven weeks, and I know your estate so well
I need hardly go out at all.
A superhighway seals me off.
Trading their poisons, the north and south bound cars
Flatten the doped snakes to ribbon. In here, the grasses
Unload their griefs on my shoes,

The woods creak and ache, and the day forgets itself.
I bend over this drained basin where the small fish
Flex as the mud freezes.
They glitter like eyes, and I collect them all.
Morgue of old logs and old images, the lake
Opens and shuts, accepting them among its reflections.

Widow

Widow. The word consumes itself—
Body, a sheet of newsprint on the fire
Levitating a numb minute in the updraft
Over the scalding, red topography
That will put her heart out like an only eye.

Widow. The dead syllable, with its shadow
Of an echo, exposes the panel in the wall
Behind which the secret passage lies—stale air,
Fusty remembrances, the coiled-spring stair
That opens at the top onto nothing at all. . . .

Widow. The bitter spider sits
And sits in the centre of her loveless spokes.
Death is the dress she wears, her hat and collar.
The moth-face of her husband, moonwhite and ill,
Circles her like a prey she'd love to kill

A second time, to have him near again—
A paper image to lay against her heart
The way she laid his letters, till they grew warm
And seemed to give her warmth, like a live skin.
But it is she who is paper now, warmed by no-one.

Widow: that great, vacant estate!
The voice of God is full of draughtiness,
Promising simply the hard stars, the space
Of immortal blankness between stars
And no bodies, singing like arrows up to heaven.

Widow, the compassionate trees bend in,
The trees of loneliness, the trees of mourning.
They stand like shadows about the green landscape—
Or even like black holes cut out of it.
A widow resembles them, a shadow-thing,

Hand folding hand, and nothing in between.
A bodiless soul could pass another soul
In this clear air and never notice it—
One soul pass through the other, frail as smoke
And utterly ignorant of the way it took.

That is the fear she has—the fear
His soul may beat and be beating at her dull sense
Like blue Mary's angel, dovelike against a pane
Blinded to all but the grey, spiritless room
It looks in on, and must go on looking in on.

Tulips

The tulips are too excitable, it is winter here.
Look how white everything is, how quiet, how
snowed-in.
I am learning peacefulness, lying by myself quietly
As the light lies on these white walls, this bed, these
hands.
I am nobody; I have nothing to do with explosions.
I have given my name and my day-clothes up to the
nurses
And my history to the anaesthetist and my body to
surgeons.

They have propped my head between the pillow and
the sheet-cuff
Like an eye between two white lids that will not shut.
Stupid pupil, it has to take everything in.
The nurses pass and pass, they are no trouble,
They pass the way gulls pass inland in their white caps,
Doing things with their hands, one just the same as
another,
So it is impossible to tell how many there are.

My body is a pebble to them, they tend it as water
Tends to the pebbles it must run over, smoothing them
gently.
They bring me numbness in their bright needles, they
bring me sleep.
Now I have lost myself I am sick of baggage—
My patent leather overnight case like a black pillbox,
My husband and child smiling out of the family photo;
Their smiles catch onto my skin, little smiling hooks.

I have let things slip, a thirty-year-old cargo boat
Stubbornly hanging on to my name and address.
They have swabbed me clear of my loving associations.
Scared and bare on the green plastic-pillowed trolley
I watched my teaset, my bureaus of linen, my books
Sink out of sight, and the water went over my head.
I am a nun now, I have never been so pure.

I didn't want any flowers, I only wanted
To lie with my hands turned up and be utterly empty.
How free it is, you have no idea how free——
The peacefulness is so big it dazes you,
And it asks nothing, a name tag, a few trinkets.
It is what the dead close on, finally; I imagine them
Shutting their mouths on it, like a Communion tablet.

The tulips are too red in the first place, they hurt me.
Even through the gift paper I could hear them breathe
Lightly, through their white swaddlings, like an awful
baby.
Their redness talks to my wound, it corresponds.
They are subtle: they seem to float, though they weigh
me down,
Upsetting me with their sudden tongues and their colour,
A dozen red lead sinkers round my neck.

Nobody watched me before, now I am watched.
The tulips turn to me, and the window behind me
Where once a day the light slowly widens and slowly
thins,
And I see myself, flat, ridiculous, a cut-paper shadow
Between the eye of the sun and the eyes of the tulips,
And I have no face, I have wanted to efface myself.
The vivid tulips eat my oxygen.

Before they came the air was calm enough,
Coming and going, breath by breath, without any fuss.
Then the tulips filled it up like a loud noise.
Now the air snags and eddies round them the way a river
Snags and eddies round a sunken rust-red engine.
They concentrate my attention, that was happy
Playing and resting without committing itself.

The walls, also, seem to be warming themselves.
The tulips should be behind bars like dangerous animals;
They are opening like the mouth of some great
African cat,
And I am aware of my heart: it opens and closes
Its bowl of red blooms out of sheer love of me.
The water I taste is warm and salt, like the sea,
And comes from a country far away as health.

Sheep in Fog

The hills step off into whiteness.
People or stars
Regard me sadly, I disappoint them.

The train leaves a line of breath.
O slow
Horse the colour of rust,

Hooves, dolorous bells——
All morning the
Morning has been blackening,

A flower left out.
My bones hold a stillness, the far
Fields melt my heart.

They threaten
To let me through to a heaven
Starless and fatherless, a dark water.

The Moon and the Yew Tree

This is the light of the mind, cold and planetary.
The trees of the mind are black. The light is blue.
The grasses unload their griefs on my feet as if I were
God,
Prickling my ankles and murmuring of their humility.
Fumey, spiritous mists inhabit this place
Separated from my house by a row of headstones.
I simply cannot see where there is to get to.

The moon is no door. It is a face in its own right,
White as a knuckle and terribly upset.
It drags the sea after it like a dark crime; it is quiet
With the O-gape of complete despair. I live here.
Twice on Sunday, the bells startle the sky——
Eight great tongues affirming the Resurrection.
At the end, they soberly bong out their names.

The yew tree points up. It has a Gothic shape.
The eyes lift after it and find the moon.
The moon is my mother. She is not sweet like Mary.
Her blue garments unloose small bats and owls.
How I would like to believe in tenderness——
The face of the effigy, gentled by candles,
Bending, on me in particular, its mild eyes.

I have fallen a long way. Clouds are flowering
Blue and mystical over the face of the stars.
Inside the church, the saints will be all blue,
Floating on their delicate feet over the cold pews,
Their hands and faces stiff with holiness.
The moon sees nothing of this. She is bald and wild.
And the message of the yew tree is blackness—
    blackness and silence.

Child

Your clear eye is the one absolutely beautiful thing.
I want to fill it with colour and ducks,
The zoo of the new

Whose names you meditate—
April snowdrop, Indian pipe,
Little

Stalk without wrinkle,
Pool in which images
Should be grand and classical

Not this troublous
Wringing of hands, this dark
Ceiling without a star.

Notes

BLACK ROOK IN RAINY WEATHER

The poet's life is a 'dull, ruinous landscape' under 'desultory weather' in a 'season/Of fatigue'. The sight of the rook in the rain seems to cut through this lethargy of meaninglessness (where there is a real danger of 'total neutrality')—suddenly and briefly something seems to have identity. But such moments are rare.

Notice the delicate, dry rhyming—the same or similar sound occurs at the end of the corresponding line in each stanza, giving a measure of control and pattern to the long, listless sentences. The last words of every fifth line just about tell the story of the poem.

MEDALLION

The dead snake becomes 'pure death's-metal', a 'medallion' seen in terms of bronze, glass, jewels, stone and chainmail. The poem glitters and may seem, by Sylvia Plath's standards, safely external; but the vision is of a perfection of cruelty. Note again the controlled verse: seven-syllable lines and an interlaced half-rhyme scheme, leading quietly onwards.

CROSSING THE WATER

snag: stump of old tree sticking out of the water.

sirens: beautiful water-goddesses luring sailors to destruction—traditionally, by song; here, by silence.

BLACKBERRYING

An experience most of us would find gentle and delighting—blackberrying in a country lane near the sea—is to the disturbed poet's mind a horror. Physical sensation becomes an onslaught and seems personally directed at the solitary individual (the panic begins with the first words—'Nobody in the lane'). The technique is still assured, the sentences of horror steady in the full lines, and a certain discipline maintained by the stanzaic structure—three groups of nine lines, each a different stage in the experience. The combination of proportion and ferocity reminds me above all of Van Gogh's last paintings.

PRIVATE GROUND

The poet has been staying eleven weeks on a private estate in New York State. Her private world has associated itself with the 'private ground'; and now everything is being closed up and drained for the winter. . . .

WIDOW

A study of isolation—not the poet's own but well understood by this poet. The poem takes almost the form of variations on a theme—in the early stanzas, exploring the word and its associations; later, exploring the isolation and the weird fantasy-fears it brings.

TULIPS

The poet in hospital, supposed to be recovering from breakdown, writes a terrifyingly calm and lucid account of her view of her experience. Compare Robert Lowell's poem WAKING IN THE BLUE (MODERN POETS THREE) or Sylvia Plath's own novel THE BELL JAR.

THE MOON AND THE YEW TREE

A contrast between the comforts and consolations of Christianity and the pagan starkness of the imagery of the poet's mind.

Seamus Heaney

Seamus Heaney was born in 1939 and brought up on a farm in Co. Derry, the eldest of eight children. Unlike most of his family he chose an academic training, and he has been a university lecturer in English. As soon as his first book of poetry was published in 1966 he was recognized as a distinctive and gifted writer; three subsequent books and many successful poetry readings and public appearances have confirmed him as one of our most popular and respected poets.

Heaney writes about the tragedy of his own country: the bitter and fruitless hostility between Protestant and Catholic is part of his own upbringing and he traces it in some poems, rather numbly (he has been most careful to avoid sensationalism or a cheap political 'commitment'). But his work shows that the tragedy of Ulster goes far back, within the general tragedy of Ireland. And most fundamentally perhaps Heaney writes about industrial man's loss of 'the hold of the home and the land', how 'the old traditional community which I knew as a child has disappeared'.

Heaney's poetry is about trying to do justice to, and even to cope with, such history and such loss. It is not defeated, like that of Philip Larkin, but neither is it achieving: poem after poem reaches honourably *towards* what might be adequate statement (and therefore grand statement, since the tragedies are major). Many Heaney poems are about how he is hoping to write poetry; it is as if he is preparing himself for a major work, not because he will necessarily be capable of it but because to settle for less would be ignoble. The final poem in this selection sums up with characteristic integrity and delicacy this position. Paradoxically it is in this relative dejection that he seems nearest to Yeatsian sharpness. He is a poet whose main development may still lie ahead.

Digging

Between my finger and my thumb
The squat pen rests; snug as a gun.

Under my window, a clean rasping sound
When the spade sinks into gravelly ground:
My father, digging. I look down

Till his straining rump among the flowerbeds
Bends low, comes up twenty years away
Stooping in rhythm through potato drills
Where he was digging.

The coarse boot nestled on the lug, the shaft
Against the inside knee was levered firmly.
He rooted out tall tops, buried the bright edge deep
To scatter new potatoes that we picked
Loving their cool hardness in our hands.

By God, the old man could handle a spade.
Just like his old man.

My grandfather cut more turf in a day
Than any other man on Toner's bog.
Once I carried him milk in a bottle
Corked sloppily with paper. He straightened up
To drink it, then fell to right away
Nicking and slicing neatly, heaving sods
Over his shoulder, going down and down
For the good turf. Digging.

The cold smell of potato mould, the squelch and slap
Of soggy peat, the curt cuts of an edge
Through living roots awaken in my head.
But I've no spade to follow men like them.

Between my finger and my thumb
The squat pen rests.
I'll dig with it.

Death of a Naturalist

All year the flax-dam festered in the heart
Of the townland; green and heavy headed
Flax had rotted there, weighted down by huge sods.
Daily it sweltered in the punishing sun.
Bubbles gargled delicately, bluebottles
Wove a strong gauze of sound around the smell.
There were dragon-flies, spotted butterflies,
But best of all was the warm thick slobber
Of frogspawn that grew like clotted water
In the shade of the banks. Here, every spring
I would fill jampotfuls of the jellied
Specks to range on window-sills at home,
On shelves at school, and wait and watch until
The fattening dots burst into nimble-
Swimming tadpoles. Miss Walls would tell us how
The daddy frog was called a bullfrog
And how he croaked and how the mammy frog
Laid hundreds of little eggs and this was
Frogspawn. You could tell the weather by frogs too
For they were yellow in the sun and brown
In rain.

Then one hot day when fields were rank
With cowdung in the grass the angry frogs
Invaded the flax-dam; I ducked through hedges
To a coarse croaking that I had not heard
Before. The air was thick with a bass chorus.
Right down the dam gross-bellied frogs were cocked
On sods; their loose necks pulsed like sails. Some hopped:
The slap and plop were obscene threats. Some sat
Poised like mud grenades, their blunt heads farting.
I sickened, turned, and ran. The great slime kings
Were gathered there for vengeance and I knew
That if I dipped my hand the spawn would clutch it.

At a Potato Digging

I

A mechanical digger wrecks the drill,
Spins up a dark shower of roots and mould.
Labourers swarm in behind, stoop to fill
Wicker creels. Fingers go dead in the cold.

Like crows attacking crow-black fields, they stretch
A higgledy line from hedge to headland;
Some pairs keep breaking ragged ranks to fetch
A full creel to the pit and straighten, stand

Tall for a moment but soon stumble back
To fish a new load from the crumbled surf.
Heads bow, trunks bend, hands fumble towards the black
Mother. Processional stooping through the turf

Recurs mindlessly as autumn. Centuries
Of fear and homage to the famine god
Toughen the muscles behind their humbled knees,
Make a seasonal altar of the sod.

II

Flint-white, purple. They lie scattered
like inflated pebbles. Native
to the black hutch of clay
where the halved seed shot and clotted
these knobbed and slit-eyed tubers seem
the petrified hearts of drills. Split
by the spade, they show white as cream.

Good smells exude from crumbled earth.
The rough bark of humus erupts
knots of potatoes (a clean birth)
whose solid feel, whose wet inside
promises taste of ground and root.
To be piled in pits; live skulls, blind-eyed.

III

Live skulls, blind-eyed, balanced on
wild higgledy skeletons
scoured the land in 'forty-five,
wolfed the blighted root and died.

The new potato, sound as stone,
putrefied when it had lain
three days in the long clay pit.
Millions rotted along with it.

Mouths tightened in, eyes died hard,
faces chilled to a plucked bird.
In a million wicker huts
beaks of famine snipped at guts.

A people hungering from birth,
grubbing, like plants, in the bitch earth,
were grafted with a great sorrow.
Hope rotted like a marrow.

Stinking potatoes fouled the land,
pits turned pus into filthy mounds:
and where potato diggers are
you still smell the running sore.

IV

Under a gay flotilla of gulls
The rhythm deadens, the workers stop.
Brown bread and tea in bright canfuls
Are served for lunch. Dead-beat, they flop

Down in the ditch and take their fill,
Thankfully breaking timeless fasts;
Then, stretched on the faithless ground, spill
Libations of cold tea, scatter crusts.

The Play Way

Sunlight pillars through glass, probes each desk
For milk-tops, drinking straws and old dry crusts.
The music strides to challenge it
Mixing memory and desire with chalk dust.

My lesson notes read: Teacher will play
Beethoven's Concerto Number Five
And class will express themselves freely
In writing. One said 'Can we jive?'

When I produced the record, but now
The big sound has silenced them. Higher
And firmer, each authoritative note
Pumps the classroom up tight as a tyre

Working its private spell behind eyes
That stare wide. They have forgotten me
For once. The pens are busy, the tongues mime
Their blundering embrace of the free

Word. A silence charged with sweetness
Breaks short on lost faces where I see
New looks. Then notes stretch taut as snares. They trip
To fall into themselves unknowingly.

Mother

As I work at the pump, the wind heavy
With spits of rain is fraying
The rope of water I'm pumping.
It pays itself out like air's afterbirth
At each gulp of the plunger.

I am tired of the feeding of stock.
Each evening I labour this handle
Half an hour at a time, the cows
Guzzling at bowls in the byre.
Before I have topped up the level
They lower it down.

They've trailed in again by the readymade gate
He stuck into the fence: a jingling bedhead
Wired up between posts. It's on its last legs.
It does not jingle for joy any more.

I am tired of walking about with this plunger
Inside me. God, he plays like a young calf
Gone wild on a rope.
Lying or standing won't settle these capers,
This gulp in my well.

O when I am a gate for myself
Let such wind fray my waters
As scarfs my skirt through my thighs,
Stuffs air down my throat.

Whinlands

All year round the whin
Can show a blossom or two
But it's in full bloom now.
As if the small yolk stain

From all the birds' eggs in
All the nests of the spring
Were spiked and hung
Everywhere on bushes to ripen.

Hills oxidize gold.
Above the smoulder of green shoot
And dross of dead thorns underfoot
The blossoms scald.

Put a match under
Whins, they go up of a sudden.
They make no flame in the sun
But a fierce heat tremor

Yet incineration like that
Only takes the thorn.
The tough sticks don't burn,
Remain like bone, charred horn.

Gilt, jaggy, springy, frilled
This stunted, dry richness
Persists on hills, near stone ditches,
Over flintbed and battlefield.

'This morning from a dewy motorway'

This morning from a dewy motorway
I saw the new camp for the internees:
a bomb had left a crater of fresh clay
in the roadside, and over in the trees

machine-gun posts defined a real stockade.
There was that white mist you get on a low ground
and it was déjà-vu, some film made
of Stalag 17, a bad dream with no sound.

Is there a life before death? That's chalked up
on a wall downtown. Competence with pain,
coherent miseries, a bite and sup,
we hug our little destiny again.

Linen Town

High Street, Belfast, 1786

It's twenty to four
By the public clock. A cloaked rider
Clops off into an entry

Coming perhaps from the Linen Hall
Or Cornmarket
Where, the civic print unfrozen,

In twelve years' time
They hanged young McCracken—
This lownecked belle and tricorned fop's

Still flourish undisturbed
By the swinging tongue of his body.
Pen and ink, water tint

Fence and fetch us in
Under bracketed tavern signs,
The edged gloom of arcades.

It's twenty to four
On one of the last afternoons
Of reasonable light.

Smell the tidal Lagan:
Take a last turn
In the tang of possibility.

The Seed Cutters

They seem hundreds of years away. Breughel,
You'll know them if I can get them true.
They kneel under the hedge in a half-circle
Behind a windbreak wind is breaking through.
They are the seed cutters. The tuck and frill
Of leaf-sprout is on the seed potatoes
Buried under that straw. With time to kill
They are taking their time. Each sharp knife goes
Lazily halving each root that falls apart
In the palm of the hand: a milky gleam,
And, at the centre, a dark watermark.
O calendar customs! Under the broom
Yellowing over them, compose the frieze
With all of us there, our anonymities.

North

I returned to a long strand,
the hammered shod of a bay,
and found only the secular
powers of the Atlantic thundering.

I faced the unmagical
invitations of Iceland,
the pathetic colonies
of Greenland, and suddenly

those fabulous raiders,
those lying in Orkney and Dublin
measured against
their long swords rusting,

those in the solid
belly of stone ships,
those hacked and glinting
in the gravel of thawed streams

were ocean-deafened voices
warning me, lifted again
in violence and epiphany.
The longship's swimming tongue

was buoyant with hindsight—
it said Thor's hammer swung
to geography and trade,
thick-witted couplings and revenges,

the hatreds and behindbacks
of the althing, lies and women,
exhaustions nominated peace,
memory incubating the spilled blood.

It said, 'Lie down
in the word-hoard, burrow
the coil and gleam
of your furrowed brain.

Compose in darkness.
Expect aurora borealis
in the long foray
but no cascade of light.

Keep your eye clear
as the bleb of the icicle,
trust the feel of what nubbed treasure
your hands have known.'

Summer 1969

While the Constabulary covered the mob
Firing into the Falls, I was suffering
Only the bullying sun of Madrid.
Each afternoon, in the casserole heat
Of the flat, as I sweated my way through
The life of Joyce, stinks from the fishmarket
Rose like the reek off a flax-dam.
At night on the balcony, gules of wine,
A sense of children in their dark corners,
Old women in black shawls near open windows,
The air a canyon rivering in Spanish.
We talked our way home over starlit plains
Where patent leather of the Guardia Civil
Gleamed like fish-bellies in flax-poisoned waters.

'Go back,' one said, 'try to touch the people.'
Another conjured Lorca from his hill.
We sat through death counts and bullfight reports
On the television, celebrities
Arrived from where the real thing still happened.

I retreated to the cool of the Prado.
Goya's 'Shootings of the Third of May'
Covered a wall—the thrown-up arms
And spasm of the rebel, the helmeted

And knapsacked military, the efficient
Rake of the fusillade. In the next room
His nightmares, grafted to the palace wall—
Dark cyclones, hosting, breaking; Saturn
Jewelled in the blood of his own children,
Gigantic Chaos turning his brute hips
Over the world. Also, that holmgang
Where two berserks club each other to death
For honour's sake, greaved in a bog, and sinking.

He painted with his fists and elbows, flourished
The stained cape of his heart as history charged.

Exposure

It is December in Wicklow:
Alders dripping, birches
Inheriting the last light,
The ash tree cold to look at.

A comet that was lost
Should be visible at sunset,
Those million tons of light
Like a glimmer of haws and rose-hips,

And I sometimes see a falling star.
If I could come on meteorite!
Instead I walk through damp leaves,
Husks, the spent flukes of autumn,

Imagining a hero
On some muddy compound,
His gift like a slingstone
Whirled for the desperate.

How did I end up like this?
I often think of my friends'
Beautiful prismatic counselling
And the anvil brains of some who hate me

As I sit weighing and weighing
My responsible *tristia*.
For what? For the ear? For the people?
For what is said behind-backs?

Rain comes down through the alders,
Its low conducive voices
Mutter about let-downs and erosions
And yet each drop recalls

The diamond absolutes.
I am neither internee nor informer;
An inner émigré, grown long-haired
And thoughtful; a wood-kerne

Escaped from the massacre,
Taking protective colouring
From bole and bark, feeling
Every wind that blows;

Who, blowing up these sparks
For their meagre heat, have missed
The once-in-a-lifetime portent,
The comet's pulsing rose.

Notes

DIGGING
The first poem in Seamus Heaney's first volume: the poet pledges himself to try to make poems with the same skill and perseverance his father and grandfather gave to digging.

DEATH OF A NATURALIST
Real life—real nature—is not miniature or pretty, as schoolroom nature study might make it seem. The poet good-humouredly recalls an early failure of nerve: a small child's encounter with and flight from sexuality, inseparable at that age from stink, slime and excretion. The mature poet has got over that failure of nerve, and delights in the noisy and 'vulgar' language, the heaviness of natural life.

AT A POTATO DIGGING
drill: row of potatoes (the ridge of soil under which they lie).

creels: baskets.

I. Ireland has suffered 'Centuries/Of fear and homage to the famine god'. Potatoes have all too often been the main diet of her peasants. Today, even in mass gathering behind a machine, the poet feels a sense of reverence and ritual (the earth is 'the black/Mother').

II. A vivid picture of potatoes themselves.

III. A terrible description of famine in the 1840s, bitterly introduced by the use in its literal sense of a metaphor from the last line of II.

IV. Back to the modern potato-digging; the full significance of the occasion now clear to the reader. What is the point of the last two lines?

THE PLAY WAY

The title is a half-ironic reference to modern educational theory. It seems as if the poet quite expected the music to fail (the bluntness of 'with chalk dust', the ironic note of a pupil's 'Can we jive?'). Instead, it works. The imagery of the poem, without being flashy, is expressive and persuasive: 'strides' (line 3), 'Pumps the classroom up tight as a tyre' (line 12)—if you know Beethoven, and particularly this concerto, you will see exactly what is meant. The children's tongues wriggling round their lips as they write are seen by the poet as miming their discovery of the creative word. Best of all, the last two lines: the music catches the children unaware, reveals parts of themselves they did not know about.

MOTHER

The pregnant woman working on the farm sees her work in images of her 'labour' in childbirth, and the pregnancy and childbirth in images of the farm and the landscape. The farm-labour and the birth-labour are a unity in her life. It is a rough life and a sardonic, heavy tone is appropriate—her dry observation of the bedhead/gate is perfect here—but there is nothing ironic about her prayer in the last four lines: may the childbirth go powerfully, quickly, easily. The energy and matter-of-factness of the poem's rhythms and language carry it far from sentimentality; yet it is a portrait charged with compassion and respect.

WHINLANDS

Whin is gorse. Images of pain and violence make this a harsh celebration of vegetation of a harsh landscape. Heaney here is content to imply ('bone', 'charred horn', 'battlefield') the associations we might find in the landscape. Courage? Sheer survival?

'THIS MORNING FROM A DEWY MOTORWAY'

These lines are the epigraph to Heaney's third volume,

WINTERING OUT, and are part of a longer poem in his fourth volume NORTH.

déjà-vu: seen before somewhere.

LINEN TOWN

Belfast before things started to go wrong. The poem seems based on an ink and water-colour painting, which explains why the fop's 'flourish' in the eighteenth-century street, a 'lownecked belle' alongside him, is 'still'. The shadow of the future is in the poet's hindsight only.

THE SEED CUTTERS

The second of two poems which stand as introduction to Heaney's fourth volume. The form is the 'Shakespearean' sonnet. *Breughel* is the most powerful and convincing of the sixteenth-century Dutch painters of peasant life. *Frieze* in the penultimate line again invites us to see the seed cutters as part of some ancient painting (and the old-style vocative 'O calendar customs!' has a similar effect)—but it is a painting which involves ourselves. From the observer's dispassionate distance ('get them true') through a wry pity (the wind *is* breaking through what is supposed to be a windbreak) the poem becomes, at the end, an attempt to link poet and reader, as anonymous mankind, to the peasants. Silently implied is the difficulty of feeling such a link, the probable discontinuity between the rural life and the relatively sophisticated life of people likely to read or write this sort of poetry.

NORTH

Title poem of Heaney's fourth volume. The Northern Irish poet abandons the Icelandic and Nordic stories as a possible mythology to direct or vitalize his work. *Hindsight* sees the sagas as based upon ordinary and ignoble human greed, meanness, and sheer economics; to try to forget this hindsight would be dishonest. The 'north journey' of Seamus

Heaney has to be like a hibernation, introspective; it will be primarily a matter of clear vision—truth-telling—and sound experience, even if that experience is limited (the 'treasure/ your hands have known' is what matters, not the unattainable loot of the saga-heroes). There will be no flood of daylight, but in the long northern night the strange beauties of the northern lights may shine. Poetry but not revelation? At any rate the poem commits the poet to a long, unromantic, and honest haul.

hammered shod: the bay is in the shape of a horse-shoe. Heaney's phrasing introduces the imagery of metal and violence.

secular: not religious or mythological.

epiphany: moment of truth.

althing: assembly.

nominated: called by the name of.

incubating: warming (what was really cold).

bleb: bubble in glass.

SUMMER 1969

The fourth of a series of six poems in which Heaney tries to relate himself to his troubled times. In 1969 events in Northern Ireland became much more violent. Heaney, in Spain, wondering how his own poetry should or could help his people in this situation, considers the example of the great Spanish painter Goya, who, from being an exquisite depicter of the calm aristocratic scene, responded to political horror by new and terrible paintings (try to find reproductions of them).

Falls: the Falls Road (Catholic area of Belfast).

bullying: the sound prepares us for the 'bullfight reports' later and the magnificent matador epigram of the last two lines.

Joyce: a great Irish writer who left his country permanently and did not involve himself in its political disturbances.

like the reek off a flax-dam: see DEATH OF A NATURALIST, and also the line at the end of this verse-paragraph. A childhood symbol of industry poisoning the environment is attached to the Ulster Constabulary and the Spanish Guardia Civil.

gules: red colour.

conjured Lorca from his hill: called up the memory of a great Spanish poet and playwright who did enter into political action.

Prado: art gallery in Madrid.

hosting: perhaps, gathering like an army.

holmgang: a duel to the death.

greaved: literally, with bog as shin-guards; in other words, up to their knees in bog.

EXPOSURE

The last poem in the same sequence. The poet considers his own poetry and is depressed about its lack of 'once-in-a-lifetime portent'. His work is decent, sad, and minor ('responsible *tristia*'). He would like to blaze in the sky like a comet, whirl his gift round his head like a desperate hero. The rain seems to offer explanations and relative judgements—perhaps that heroic poetry is no longer possible—and yet the glitter of each raindrop recalls the possibility of absolute values. The poet has not fought and been interned; nor has he betrayed his people either. He has not emigrated (like Joyce in the previous poem) but he has withdrawn so far into himself that it is like an emigration, or like becoming an elf of the woods (*wood-kerne*).

ACKNOWLEDGEMENTS

Acknowledgements are due to the following for permission to publish copyright material: Faber & Faber Ltd for poems by Philip Larkin from *The North Ship*, *The Whitsun Weddings* and *High Windows*; Faber & Faber Ltd for poems by Thom Gunn from *Fighting Terms*, *The Sense of Movement*, *My Sad Captains*, *Touch* and *Jack Straw's Castle*; Faber & Faber Ltd for poems by Ted Hughes from *Lupercal*, *The Hawk in the Rain*, *Wodwo*, *Crow*, *Season Songs* and *Gaudete*; Miss Olwyn Hughes for the following poems by Sylvia Plath: 'Black Rook in Rainy Weather' and 'Medallion' from *The Colossus*, 'Crossing the Water', 'Blackberrying', 'Private Ground' and 'Widow' from *Crossing the Water*, 'Tulips', 'Sheep in the Fog' and 'The Moon and the Yew Tree' from *Ariel* and 'Child' from *Winter Trees* (all published by Faber & Faber Ltd); Faber & Faber Ltd for poems by Seamus Heaney from *Death of a Naturalist*, *Door into the Dark*, *Wintering Out* and *North*. 'Wedding-Wind' and 'Church-Going' by Philip Larkin are reprinted from *The Less Deceived* by permission of The Marvell Press, England. The following poems by Charles Tomlinson are published by permission of the author and Oxford University Press: 'How Still the Hawk' and 'Winter Encounters' from *Seeing is Believing*, 1960, 'What it was like' and 'How it happened' from *A Peopled Landscape*, 1963, 'The Weathercocks' and 'On a Mexican Straw Christ' from *American Scenes*, 1966, 'Swimming Chenango Lake', 'Against Extremity', 'A Sense of Distance' and 'The Chances of Rhyme' from *The Way of a World*, 1969, 'Night Ride', 'The Rich', 'Foxes' Moon' and 'In December' from *The Way In*, 1974, 'Rhymes' and 'Images of Perfection' from *The Shaft*, 1978.

In the case of certain poems by Ted Hughes, acknowledgements to include them in this collection for use in Canada are made to Harper & Row, Publishers, Inc., for 'Wind' copyright © 1956 by Ted Hughes, 'The Thought-Fox' copyright © 1957 by Ted Hughes and 'The Jaguar' copyright © 1957 by Ted Hughes (all from *The Hawk in the Rain*).

But she was hard put to it to keep her vow never to speak to him again. Eden bit down a string of heated words, and marched to the reception area.

It was then that she learned what it felt like to be ignored, for the male night receptionist-cum-night porter looked not to her, but to the man who had come in with her.

'Good evening, sir,' he said smartly.

'I'd like a room,' Sterne replied, and although she would not look at him, Eden knew that he was looking at her when he added, 'For one night only, I think.'

The receptionist was all attention, and Eden guessed wearily that Sterne Parnell was the type who would always have someone ready to jump to attention for him. 'Certainly, sir,' he replied. 'A double room?' he enquired.

It was Eden's turn to snap to attention. '*We*—are not together,' she told the man icily. She would have added that she required accommodation as far away as possible from the man who had just chanced to walk through the door at the same time when Sterne Parnell spoke.

'It would appear that I shall be sleeping on my own tonight,' he told the man behind the desk. Eden jerked her head round in amazement at the implication in his words, but only to have her amazement added to, when looking at the man she had known mainly as a terse brute, she saw that the very devil was dancing in his eyes!

Books you will enjoy
by JESSICA STEELE

RELATIVE STRANGERS

Stein Kildedalen thought Zarah was a gold-digger but she knew it wasn't true. All she wanted from this visit to Norway was to solve the mystery of her parentage.

UNFRIENDLY ALLIANCE

When Anstey was literally left holding the baby—her friend's baby—she decided the only thing she could do was turn for help to the child's uncle, the forbidding Cale Quartermaine. But how far could she trust a man like him?

FORTUNES OF LOVE

BY

JESSICA STEELE

MILLS & BOON LIMITED
ETON HOUSE 18-24 PARADISE ROAD
RICHMOND SURREY TW9 1SR

First published in Great Britain 1988
by Mills & Boon Limited

This edition 1988

ISBN 0 263 75931 8

Set in Times Roman 10 on 11½pt.
01–0388-56229 C

Printed and bound in Great Britain by
Collins, Glasgow

CHAPTER ONE

EDEN finished her ablutions in the bathroom and went to the sitting-room with the intention of saying good-night to her stepbrother. His troubled expression, though, stopped her.

'Don't look so worried, love,' she said quickly, and delayed going to bed, by taking the 'seen better days' chair opposite him. 'Camilla will have told her guardian all about you by now, and no one, not even Sterne Parnell, could have any objection to you.'

'That's what I keep telling myself,' Thomas replied, raising a smile. 'Only I can't help feeling that I should be with her when Camilla tells him that in the six weeks he's been away we've met, fallen in love, and want to get married.'

'But I thought it was your suggestion that, since Camilla's guardian would probably be not only jet-lagged but over-worked into the bargain, he'd feel more like putting his feet up this evening than entertaining his ward's suitor?'

'So it was,' Thomas nodded. 'But only after Camilla had vetoed my first suggestion—which was that I'd request an interview with him tomorrow, and ask his permission to marry her then.'

'Camilla couldn't wait until tomorrow to tell her guardian your good news?' Eden teased.

Thomas had to grin. 'That's about it,' he said. 'And I must have consented.' He shook his head as if he had no memory of agreeing to allow Camilla to speak to her guardian on his behalf, and then warned his stepsister,

'You wait until it happens to you, Eden Glendening-Smith. One minute you know yourself to be sane and the most logical-thinking person you know. Then, hey presto, Cupid lets go his dart and, love-crazy, you find any powers of logical thinking you had have gone.'

'Sounds like something I could do with missing out on,' Eden said sunnily, and as she observed that Thomas was looking more cheerful, she left her chair and went to lightly kiss his cheek. 'It'll soon be tomorrow,' she told him. ''Night, love,' she added, and, smiling, she went to bed.

She could find nothing to smile about ten minutes later, however. She was in the process of brushing her 'pump-water' straight white-blonde hair when sad memories started to penetrate her thinking. From her initial thought—how good it was that Thomas was going to be happy after the dreadful time he had been through—she was soon remembering. Remembering—how dreadful it had been, for them both.

Eden had no memory of her mother who had died when she was a toddler. Her memory of her first ten years of life was that life was a pretty solemn affair. Then her father had married warm-hearted Ruth Morrisey. Ruth and her twelve-year-old son had moved into the Manor, and suddenly Eden's father, a man she could seldom remember seeing smile, was all at once full of laughter.

She recalled how she had quickly taken to Ruth's warmth. Of Ruth's son, though, she was not at first sure. But she had soon discovered that her stepbrother was not the same as the brothers of the girls at school. For where they pulled hair and made their sisters fetch and carry for them and were quite totally horrid by the sound of it, her stepbrother was different. Thomas, she found, was a gentle, caring person.

Thomas had stayed gentle and caring and over the next twelve years a bond grew between them. And they had clung as though they were flesh and blood brother and sister when, eight months ago, tragedy had struck.

Eden went back to a year ago when her stepmother, as she did every October, started suffering again with bronchitis. That October, her father decided to do something about it.

'We're moving,' he announced to the two offspring present, 'to warmer climes.'

'We...' Eden, the first to recover, uttered, and as what he said unravelled in her head she exclaimed, 'We're going to live abroad!'

'I've said we will every year when Ruth gets laid low. This bout she has now seems worse than ever—and it's only the start of our winter! You two,' he added, as if it was of no concern to him, though they both knew better, 'you want to come too?'

'Like a shot,' said Thomas, who was stuck in a job he didn't like, but did not want to give offence by handing in his notice without good reason. 'Just say when, and I'll write out my resignation.'

'And you, Eden?' Vaughan Glendening-Smith addressed his daughter. 'Is that clothes shop you help out in going to survive without your unpaid services?'

Eden grinned at her father's teasing. 'They'll manage,' she answered. 'But in any case, we'll be back for the summer, won't...' Her father's head-shake made her break off.

'When we go, it will be for good,' he told them. 'Ruth's health is too important to be held to ransom by the vagaries of the British climate.'

'We won't be coming back?' gasped Eden, as the full import of what he was saying penetrated.

'Oh, I imagine you and Thomas will. For a holiday if nothing else,' he replied, 'but . . .'

'But not you and Mum?' Thomas stated.

'That's right.'

'But—what about the house?' Eden asked. She loved the old Manor.

'We've got to harden our hearts, Eden,' her father answered. 'The house will go, as will the furniture.'

'You're selling the furniture!' she exclaimed, and even though she could not believe that money was at the root, for her father was known to be something of a financial genius in the City, she just had to ask, 'We're not short of funds, are we?'

'Good heavens, no,' he scorned, and went on to confide, 'Ruth loves this house, as we all do, but in my view, if we no longer own the Manor, then she won't be able to hanker to come back to it.'

Realising that by selling the Manor and its contents her father was cauterising Ruth's home-sickness before it began, Eden saw that to sell it was the only way.

In the event, though, her father's efforts to get his wife out of her present climate did not move as fast as he would have liked. Both Eden and Thomas gave up their jobs in order to take from Ruth some of the strain of showing prospective purchasers over the house. They helped, too, in clearing out cupboards and attics.

A buyer for the house and its contents was not found until Christmas Eve, and by the time contracts had been signed and the sale nearing completion, it was the middle of February.

A problem arose, though, in that the new owners could not take possession until the second week in March. Winter was particularly vicious that year, and in order to ensure that the new occupants were not greeted by burst pipes or such like, they asked if someone could remain in residence until then.

'I'll stay!' Thomas immediately volunteered, as keen as the rest of them that, the die cast, his mother should know no further delay in getting to their new home in the Bahamas.

'I'll stay, too.' Eden promptly joined forces with him. 'Unlike Thomas, I haven't sold my car yet, so I can use the extra week to find someone who'll be kind to her.'

The matter was settled. But Eden did not get to sell her car.

She and Thomas had grown into the habit of referring to her father and to his mother as 'the parents'. It was snowing hard on the day they stood waving them off. They did not see them again.

Eden had been in the middle of thinking that the plane had taken off, and that soon Ruth's health would start to improve, when suddenly a police car had pulled up outside.

It was Thomas who went to the door, but one look at his ashen face when he came back, was enough to tell Eden that something dreadful had happened. 'There's been a pile-up,' he said. 'The parents—they're dead!'

The weeks that followed passed in something of a haze. Neither of them had any other relatives. Ruth's first husband had died shortly after she had divorced him, and Thomas, like Eden, had no memory of his other parent. His father, like Eden's mother, had died when he was too small to remember him.

The new owners of the house were very kind and delayed moving in until the private funeral was over. Two days after the funeral Eden and Thomas piled their personal possessions into her car and drove to take the keys of the house to the solicitors for the new owners to pick up later that day. The family solicitor, Mr Boswell, had telephoned as soon as he had heard of his clients' death, and he was on hand when they took the keys in.

'In the normal course of events, I would have written to you, anyway,' he said, 'but with you delivering the keys of the Manor, I can acquaint you with the terms of your respective parents' wills now.'

Neither of them had given thought to money, most likely because it was something which they had never had to worry over. Nor, they discovered, would they have to worry about it now. For the two wills were identical, so that if Ruth pre-deceased her husband or the other way round the outcome was just the same. Eden and Thomas learned that at the age of twenty-five they would each inherit a small fortune. In the meantime, although it was clear that neither parent had thought they would die before their offspring's twenty-fifth birthday, the trustees had the discretion to make funds available to keep them ticking over.

Outside the solicitor's office, they went to Eden's car. 'Where to?' she asked chokily as the full import of the fact that they had no home to go to suddenly hit her.

'Let's try London,' Thomas said quietly, looking near to tears himself. 'It's as anonymous there as anywhere, and I'm not yet ready to meet people I know.'

They had been in a hotel in London for a week when Thomas came to Eden's room and told her that he had found the temporary answer to their prayers.

'I'm not quite with you,' Eden told him, and was reminded.

'You know you were only saying last night that you didn't care much for hotel life, and that you would prefer we had a place of our own?'

'Yes, of course,' she replied, and was still of the same view that hotels were fine for holidays and the occasional convenience if one was away from home, but that she by far preferred a home of her own.

'Well,' said Thomas, 'I've found us a place of our own.'

'You've been out looking for...' For the first time in weeks Eden felt herself starting to get excited. 'You've found us a flat to rent!' she exclaimed in a rush.

'Sort of,' he hedged, and went on to quickly tell her that he had not actually gone out looking for a place for them to live, but that he had been in a car salesroom with a view to buying a car, when someone had called his name.

'Who do you know in London!' Eden exclaimed.

'No one, or so I thought,' Thomas replied. 'And I was certain I didn't know the scruffy-looking individual who'd called my name. But as I tried to visualise the paint-begrimed guy without his wild-looking beard, I suddenly realised he was none other than Charlie Oakes.'

'Charlie Oakes!' Eden repeated, and as her memory awakened, 'You were at school with a Charlie Oakes! Wasn't he expelled for refusing to do any lessons but the ones he wanted to do?'

'You've got him!' Thomas exclaimed, and went on to tell her that Charlie, struggling to make his way in the world as an artist, was at the car salesroom trying to offload his car before he went on a world tour. 'He asked about you, by the way,' he added.

'He remembered me!' Eden could not remember ever having met up with Charlie Oakes.

'He saw you once and told me that he's never forgotten the beauty of your terrific blue eyes.'

'Good heavens!' Eden murmured, and was put off enough to forget about the accommodation which Thomas had found, and to ask instead, 'Did he—er—sell his car?'

'He decided that the garage were robbers and not deserving of his vehicle He always was slightly bonkers,'

Thomas inserted. 'Anyway, we went to a pub and had a half, and when I'd finished telling him a bit about our circumstances, he wouldn't hear of anything but that we use his flat while he's away, and that I similarly forget about buying a car, and use his.'

A week followed during which Eden could hardly wait for Charlie Oakes to remove himself from his flat so that she and Thomas could move in.

She later supposed that Thomas's description of Charlie as a scruffy-looking individual should have warned her that his apartment might look somewhat similar. For when eventually Charlie went on his world tour, and she and Thomas carried their belongings up three flights of stairs to the attic flat, she was horrified.

'It's—filthy!' she gasped as she went in.

'And damp!' Thomas followed her in, and suddenly, perhaps because the sight of decaying food left on a plate, peeling wallpaper, and mould on walls all seemed to be something out of a horror story, they both had to laugh.

But Eden sensed that tears were near, and quickly she checked her laughter to state, 'I—just daren't look in the bedrooms, and I shudder to think what the bathroom's like.'

Somehow though, with the two of them still grieving for the parents, the sprucing up of Charlie Oakes's appalling flat seemed to be a challenge they needed.

From the moment of deciding *not* to go back to hotel living, Eden got busy. March had given way to April, with May just around the corner, when she sat back and reviewed the change in the place. The first thing she and Thomas had done was to go out and buy new bedding. Then they had man-handled the old bedding, along with anything else they could not live with, into a spare room.

The spare room was soon full and could not take so much as a stick from the sitting-room. Eden got busy with soap and water. Because the awful sitting-room furniture was Charlie's, and she thought that he must like it or he would have put in on a bonfire ages ago, she could do nothing but scrub it up a little. But whether wallpaper hanging off the walls had a certain fascination for him or whether it didn't, the wallpaper had to go. Thomas applied white emulsion to the walls, and gradually their hard work paid off in that, if still not salubrious, at least the flat was far more habitable.

It was during the first week of May that Eden began to come to terms with losing her father and her dear stepmother. About that same time she awoke one morning in what, for all her efforts, she realised was a grotty bedroom, and started to wonder what on earth she was doing there.

She was in the apology for a kitchen squeezing oranges for breakfast when Thomas joined her, and after saying good morning, he revealed that his thoughts must have been going along similar lines.

'I think, Eden,' he said thoughtfully, 'that it's time we got our lives organised.'

The 'organising' was done over the breakfast table. There could be no looking back. They must look to the future.

'I'll get a job,' declared Thomas.

'And so will I,' said Eden.

'But not a job like my last one,' Thomas stated. 'I'm going to make sure I get the right job this time.'

'Me, too,' Eden replied. 'It's not as if we have to rush into the first job offered, is it? And while we're looking for the right work,' she brought out hesitantly, 'if you don't think Charlie will be offended—I wouldn't mind looking for a place of our own.'

Thomas went along with the idea, and their talk led them into wondering if they could perhaps buy a flat somewhere. 'Do you think Mr Boswell will let us have that amount of money in advance?' he pondered.

'He might,' Eden replied. 'You'll be twenty-five in January, so it wouldn't hurt to ask.'

When they rang Mr Boswell he said he would look into it. In the meantime he saw nothing against them viewing properties for sale.

Finding the right job, and the right flat to buy, proved to be not as easy as they had imagined. Eden was still looking for both when Thomas got fixed up with a job. They had been watching for the postman since his interview for a job as a trainee manager at Parnell Industrial Designs. When the letter did arrive telling him that he had got the job and was to start work on the first of July, Eden was as thrilled for him as he was.

'I knew you'd get it!' she congratulated him enthusiastically.

'Did you? I didn't!' he beamed. 'I fully expected to be turned down on the grounds that I was a little old to start out on the trainee manager ladder. But my university qualifications must have stood me in good stead.'

Her stepbrother's job at Parnell Industrial Designs narrowed Eden's search for property to a more localised area. But she had had no luck in finding either a job for herself or a flat to purchase when, one day in the middle of August, Thomas came home from work and she immediately knew that something momentous had happened in his life.

'What...?' she began, at the trance-like expression he wore.

'What—what?' he answered sheepishly.

'What happened today?' she asked.

'Today,' he told her quietly, 'I met the girl I want to spend the rest of my life with.'

Only just did Eden manage to prevent her jaw from falling open. Thomas had had the occasional girlfriend in the past, but he had never gone overboard for any of them.

'You're—in love?' she gasped, and saw that Thomas had not until then put a label on the emotion that had taken him. Then suddenly a slow smile spread across his face.

'I rather think I am,' he said, and spent the next fifteen minutes in relating how he and Camilla Rodgers had circled into each other's orbit that day.

Camilla Rodgers was the ward of his ultimate boss, Sterne Parnell. Sterne Parnell, apparently, had left London that morning for a six-week business trip abroad. Camilla had gone along to Parnell Industrial Designs with some papers her guardian wanted his deputy to have when, turning round one of the corridors in the building, she had collided with Thomas coming from the other direction.

'Did you speak to her?' Eden asked, wanting only the best for Thomas, but fearful for him.

'Did I ever!' he replied, and had a smile on his face as he recalled, 'Poor girl, I must have quite winded her. The least I could do was to take her for a cup of coffee.'

'You took her for a cup of coffee!'

'And I'm taking her out to dinner tonight.' Eden was still recovering from astonishment at his quick work, when he said, 'Charlie's car's a disgrace—can I borrow yours?'

'Of course,' she said, and only then did it dawn on her that her stepbrother, gentle person though he was, was much the same as anyone else when something came along in his life that he really wanted. Thomas wanted Camilla—he was going straight after her!

When Thomas brought Camilla to the flat a week later, it was soon obvious to Eden that as Thomas had fallen in love at first sight, so too had Camilla. She was a pretty, dark-haired young woman, not quite eighteen, but she had eyes for no one but him, and did not even seem to notice the damp patches on the walls or the dingy furniture.

Three weeks passed before Thomas asked Camilla to marry him. He was floating on air when he told Eden that she had accepted him. 'We can't announce our engagement yet,' he said, and explained, 'I've told Camilla that we must wait for her guardian to come home first.'

Eden smiled, and was happy for him. A few days later she realised that she could be wasting her time in searching for a flat for her and Thomas. There was no reason why Camilla and Thomas shouldn't marry as soon as Sterne Parnell came home, so it was not a flat for her and her stepbrother she must find, but somewhere for herself.

She said as much to Thomas the next morning, and saw him troubled for the first time since he had met Camilla. 'I don't like the thought of you living by yourself,' he said.

'I'm looking forward to it,' she told him brightly. 'Just think of it—no more shirts to iron!' Suddenly, though, she thought of a snag. 'Oh, crumbs,' she muttered, 'I've just thought. What if Mr Boswell won't let me have an advance to buy somewhere? I shan't be twenty-five for ages!'

'Strewth, Eden!' said Thomas, sharply for him. 'Don't go worrying about money, for lord's sake! If the trustees won't play ball, I'll give you some money in January when I inherit mine. Come to think of it, you've more right to it than me anyway, since it was your father's money to begin with.'

'I've never looked on it like that!' Eden protested shortly, and realised, as he seemed to, that they were on the verge of a spat. Suddenly she changed her cross look to a smile—everything should go smoothly for Thomas at this happiest time of his life.

The sound of Thomas's bedroom door closing made Eden aware that he had just left the sitting-room and had gone to bed. She looked down at the hairbrush in her hand and realised that she had started brushing her hair ages ago, but, while she was busy with her memories, her hairbrush had lain idle.

Putting the brush down, she climbed into bed. She and Thomas had been through a dreadful time of it, losing the parents, but things were looking brighter now. On her own front, she had an appointment on Tuesday to view the most idyllic-sounding little cottage, and had great hopes of her search for somewhere amenable to live being over. On Thomas's front, he was in love with Camilla, Camilla was in love with him. From a terrible start to the year, things were looking up.

Thomas was about first on Monday. Eden came across him polishing his shoes in the kitchen. 'Out to make an impression?' she ribbed him.

'Sterne Parnell's only been Camilla's guardian for six years, but he seems to take that duty very seriously,' Thomas replied. 'He's bound to call me up to his office this morning. He's bound to ask a pertinent question or two. Does this tie look all right?' he asked in the same breath.

His nervousness was all too obvious, and Eden made him a cup of coffee and did what she could to bolster his confidence.

'Who could possibly object to you?' she chided, and talked to him in the same vein until he went off to work.

Whenever Eden thought of Thomas that day, a smile would tease her beautifully shaped mouth. Thomas was the dearest love, and she defied anyone to object to him.

He was in her mind again during the afternoon. Had she not been convinced that he and Camilla would be going out somewhere for a celebratory meal, she would have gone out and bought all the trimmings for a slap-up meal at home. Perhaps, she mused, Sterne Parnell would be inviting Thomas to dine at his home that evening? Either way, she was confident that she need only prepare a meal for one that night.

It worried her a little when Thomas did not come home at his normal time. She shrugged the niggle of worry away, though. This was an exciting day for him, the day he could officially announce his engagement to his beloved Camilla. It could quite well be that one or two of his colleagues had taken him off to have a congratulatory drink somewhere.

That niggle of worry had returned when eight o'clock had arrived and Thomas had not. Perhaps he'd gone straight from work to Sterne Parnell's house, she fretted. But that wasn't like Thomas! He was thoughtful and caring, and would know she would be waiting to hear all about his interview with Camilla's guardian. Certain that she knew her stepbrother better than most, Eden could not stop that niggle of worry from growing. If things had gone well, the least Thomas would have done was to have picked up a phone to tell her that he wasn't coming home first to change before he went on somewhere. If things had gone well...

The words 'if things had gone well' seemed rooted in Eden's head for the next hour, so that when, just after nine, she heard Thomas coming up the stairs she was sure, without having a clue about what could have gone wrong, that something very definitely had.

One look at him as he came through the door confirmed it. His face was devoid of colour, and not since the deaths of the parents had she seen him looking so unhappy.

'Thomas!' she exclaimed, and going over to him, 'You're frozen!' she said, startled, when close inspection revealed that what colour he did have in his face was a pinched blue.

'Hello, Eden,' he replied, and seemed to be in something of a state of shock, so that she wasted no time in urging him to a seat in front of the gas fire.

Quite desperately did she want to know what had obviously gone so very wrong, but thinking to get him warmed up first, she asked, 'Have you had anything to eat?'

'I don't want anything,' he replied, and Eden left him to hurry to the kitchen to heat up a tin of soup.

She was back in no time, handing him the steaming mug, and searching for the most tactful way to get him to talk his shock out of his system.

'Feeling warmer?' she asked. Thomas nodded. 'You must have been out in the open for ages to have got so cold,' she commented.

'I've been walking around since I left the office,' he mumbled.

That was hours ago! 'You left the office at five?' she enquired.

He shook his head. 'It was somewhere around half past, tonight,' he corrected, but seemed so vague that Eden began to fear the worst.

'Did—er—Mr Parnell—call you to his office this morning as you expected?' she asked tentatively.

'Not this morning,' he replied.

'This afternoon?' she pressed, and felt pain herself when she knew that Thomas was hurting, for a shuddering kind of sigh left him, and suddenly he began to open up.

'I waited all morning, expecting every minute to hear from him,' he confided. 'When lunch time arrived and still I heard nothing, I made myself think that, since he'd been away from his office for six weeks, he had a lot of catching up to do.'

'But it wasn't that?'

Thomas seemed to be in a world of his own, and did not appear to have heard her, for he went on, 'The afternoon dragged by with me checking my watch every few minutes, so that by the time it came to a quarter to five, I was feeling sick inside in case Camilla hadn't told him about us. I almost rang her to ask, but because deep down I knew I could trust her to do what she said she would, I didn't ring.'

'But—her guardian, Sterne Parnell, he rang you?'

'His secretary did. There were just two minutes to go before five, when I was told to report to his office.'

'As you'd known all along that she would, Camilla had told her guardian that she was in love with you and wanted to marry you?'

Thomas nodded, and was looking much older than his years when he said, 'What he wanted to know was why I wanted to marry his ward.'

'That was easily answered, surely,' said Eden. 'All you had to tell him was that you love Camilla...'

'Sterne Parnell had made his mind up in advance that I did *not* love her,' Thomas stated flatly, and as Eden stared, he continued, 'Blunt and to the point, he asked me straight out, "Is it love, or your awareness that on the day my ward marries, she comes into a fortune?"'

Gasping that anyone could speak so to her dear stepbrother, Eden strangled an angry opinion of Thomas's employer, but it took a tremendous effort for her to say evenly, 'I didn't know Camilla was an heiress.'

'I didn't either,' Thomas replied. 'Believe it or not, we've never discussed money. It just wasn't important to me, and it couldn't have been important to Camilla either.'

'But you—discussed money with Sterne Parnell,' Eden prompted. 'I mean, you put him straight and made him change his tune. You told him you would take possession of your own fortune in a little over three months' time?'

'I didn't,' Thomas said quietly. 'I never got round to it.

'You didn't!' exclaimed Eden, surprised.

'I was still trying to take in his hostile manner—which was so very different from what I had been expecting—when in the same blunt and hostile way, he slammed at me that he had no wish for his ward to have anything further to do with me, and that since she occasionally came to the office, I could consider myself off his payroll.'

'He *dismissed* you!' Hardly able to credit it, Eden could see that there was far worse to come when Thomas swallowed hard.

'The next I knew,' he said, 'was that he had passed over a cheque for a tidy sum, and was telling me, "Clear your desk, Morrisey, you're out."'

'Good grief!' Eden exclaimed, understanding now why Thomas had looked so shaken when he had come in. 'Sterne Parnell tried to—buy you off!'

'It sure as hell wasn't severance pay,' Thomas told her, and revealed how, his anger starting to rise, he had ripped the cheque in two, and had told Camilla's guardian that he didn't have enough money to buy him off.

'Good for you,' Eden said stoutly, taking a great dislike to Sterne Parnell, and backing her stepbrother's action to the hilt.

'He couldn't have been more unimpressed,' Thomas replied, and looked so anguished then that she very nearly told him not to tell her any more if remembering it upset him so. But before she could stop him, Thomas was going on, his face growing more ashen by the second as he groaned, 'God, Eden, he all but finished me when he blasted me "It runs in the family. You're greedy. Like your father—you want more."'

'Your father? You mean—your stepfather?' Eden queried, getting ready to take Sterne Parnell on and anyone else in the world who said one wrong word about her father. But Thomas shook his head, and Eden began to realise that when it came to shocks, Sterne Parnell had spared him nothing. She was shaken herself when Thomas made himself go on.

'Camilla had told her guardian my name and the fact that I was employed by him as a trainee manager, so it was a small matter to get more details of me from the personnel director. From there it was easy for him to contact a firm of private detectives and to...'

'Private detectives!' Eden couldn't believe what she was hearing.

'He made no bones about telling me what he'd done.' Thomas made her believe it. 'He didn't turn a hair as he told me how he'd given my full name and date of birth to the detective agency and told them that he wanted details of me from the day I was born, and that he wanted the information by that afternoon.'

'Good heavens!' Eden gasped in astonishment.

'By four-thirty, Sterne Parnell knew where I had been born and where my parents had been born. He also knew the fact that—that my father—died of a heart attack *only two years ago*, while he was in—prison.'

'Your father—he died—in prison!' she whispered.

'You didn't know either?' Thomas asked, and looked so cast down that Eden wished that there was something she could say or do to help him.

'Of course I didn't know!' she denied. 'I thought, like you, that your father had died shortly after your mother divorced him!'

'Well, he didn't,' Thomas sighed, sounding thoroughly demoralised. 'Sterne Parnell didn't hesitate to let me know that my father was a king among con-men, and that the sentence he was serving at the time of his death was for obtaining money by deception. He told me that if I thought I was going to get my hands on his ward's fortune by deceiving her into thinking that I loved her, I could think again. Then he showed me the door.'

'I suppose Camilla's guardian's too elderly to punch on the jaw!' opined Eden, angry on her sensitive step-brother's behalf.

'He's still a few years off forty.' Thomas killed her idea that guardians were white-haired and nearing retirement age. 'But I was too staggered by what he had just told me to want to stay to argue. I can't remember leaving his office or where I went,' he said. 'But eventually I found myself in this street, so instinct must have brought me home.'

'Oh, love,' Eden sympathised, and started to hate under-forty Sterne Parnell, that he could have reduced Thomas to the state he was in. 'But,' she said on a sudden thought, 'how do you know that the man who died in prison was your father? The private detectives could have got it wrong,' she said quickly. 'They...'

'There aren't too many Denzil Byron Morriseys born on the same day as my father.' Thomas killed another of her theories.

'He mentioned your father by name?'

Thomas nodded, and they both fell silent, and Eden searched to find something that might cheer her depressed stepbrother up.

'What about Camilla?' she asked, injecting a bright note into her voice, and hoping that mention of Camilla's name might do the trick.

'What about her?'

'Well—er—won't she be expecting you to ring her?'

'Not after Sterne Parnell's told her all he's told me.'

'You think he'll tell her about...'

'About my father being a con-man?' interrupted Thomas. 'Of course he will! All I hope is that he does it gently when he tells her that I've been conning her too, in order to get my hands on her fortune.'

Eden doubted that Sterne Parnell had a gentle bone in his body. Look at the brutal way in which he had told Thomas what he had! Of course, prompted a small, honest voice, that awful man was not aware that Thomas was in complete ignorance about his father's past, so... Abruptly Eden flattened that small honest voice. Quite clearly Sterne Parnell was a swine of the first water, but there was a very simple way in which Thomas could get the better of him.

'But you can soon prove that you're not the remotest bit interested in her fortune,' she told him quickly. 'All you have to do is tell Camilla that you inherit your own fortune when you're twenty-five! If Camilla then particularly wants her guardian's approval to marry you, he can ring your solicitor and Mr Boswell will confirm...'

'Don't!' Thomas cut her off, and there was such anguish in his voice that Eden could have cried. 'How can I marry Camilla now?' he asked, distraught. 'Now that I know I'm the son of a jail-bird?'

Eden tried her hardest to get him to see that there was no way in which he could be held responsible for his father's sins, but when she went to bed that night, she had to admit to failure. Of course he was in shock still from all he had learned, but she did so hope that by morning he would be able to see past his stated belief that he could not ask Camilla to tie herself to the son of a con-man.

Eden was up early the next morning, but Thomas was again up before her, and one look at his haggard face told her that he hadn't slept a wink. 'Toast and marmalade, or the full bacon and egg treatment?' she asked, guessing in advance that his appetite had not improved any overnight.

'Toast and marmalade will be fine.' He made the effort to appear hungry.

They were drinking coffee when Eden, deliberately keeping away from the subject of Thomas having no job to go to, sought for some way to enquire if he had any plans for that day. More by luck than anything else, for the necessity to find somewhere else to live had suddenly become much less important, she remembered that she had an appointment to view a cottage in Surrey at midday.

'Fancy coming with me to see a del. det. two-bed cott, with chmg gdns?' she asked lightly, guessing that his heart wouldn't be in anything that day.

'No, thanks,' he answered, and did his best to smile. 'But you can drop me off to collect Charlie's banger on your way if you like. It's parked near enough to the firm, but I forgot all about it la...' His voice trailed off, and Eden knew that he had gone back to the nightmare of his thoughts.

It would not have taken much for her to have cancelled her Surrey appointment altogether. But she knew that Thomas wouldn't want her to do that, and she sensed that he wanted to be by himself anyway.

After dropping him off, she headed in the direction of Surrey. Unfortunately, the tumbledown cottage, when she eventually found it, was not what she was looking for. It needed months of work repairing it, for one thing. But when Eden began to make her excuses to the vague elderly owner, it soon became apparent to her that Mrs Franklyn was starved for company. Before Eden knew it, she had accepted an invitation to stay for a cup of tea, and it was nearer two than one before she was back on the road again.

Anxious to get back to Thomas, Eden had almost made it to the flat when the performance of her car warned that she had a slow puncture. Luck was with her, however, in that the steering held up and she was able to reach the flat and park outside without mishap. Promptly, then, she forgot all about her faulty tyre. She had been sure that Charlie Oakes's banger would be parked outside too, but it wasn't!

With Thomas on her mind, Eden climbed up to the attic flat and let herself in. When she saw that a note was propped up on the mantel, it only bore out for her that Thomas was one of the kindest and most considerate persons she knew.

Anticipating that he had scribbled a few words stating where he had gone and if she should expect him to be back for dinner, Eden went over and took up the note.

Her assumption was wrong. Quickly she scanned what he had written, then, more slowly, she read the note a second time.

'Dear Eden,' Thomas had penned, 'Camilla has had an awful row with her guardian, and has left home. Because I'm sure this flat will be the first place he'll look, I'm taking her away. I'll be in touch as soon as we've got ourselves sorted out. Don't worry. Love, Thomas.'

Eden sank down on to the settee. But, the note still in her hand, she had no time to form an opinion on its contents because a furious hammering suddenly sounded on the flat door, and caused her to almost jump out of her skin.

Before she had anywhere near collected herself, the hammering came again. Thinking that it must be urgent, she quickly dropped Thomas's note to the low table in front of her, and absently dropped her shoulder bag down on top of it. The next second she was over by the door.

She had barely pulled the door open though, when, 'Who are you?' rapped the tall, dark-haired, distinguished-looking man on the other side.

Eden was taken aback to be greeted by such hostility. But suddenly she was remembering a line from Thomas's note—'I'm sure this flat will be the first place he'll look'!

She was hostile herself as she looked straight into the cold grey eyes of the under-forty male watching her. 'More to the point, who are you?' she addressed him loftily, though in actual fact, she rather thought she knew!

CHAPTER TWO

IN A few seconds Eden realised that if she intended to wait for Sterne Parnell to tell her who he was, she would have a very long wait. His arrogance was as insufferable as the rest of him, she quickly decided when, ignoring the fact that she had asked him who he was, he snarled shortly, 'Where's Morrisey?'

'What's it got to do with you where he is?' she retorted, and saw from the narrowing of his eyes that he found her irritating in the extreme. That pleased her. She smiled.

'You live here?' he asked with a jerk of his head, clearly not taken by the fact that her perfect white teeth were a dentist's dream.

'Yes, I do!' she snapped, her phoney smile abruptly fading.

'You're Morrisey's mistress!' he hurled at her. 'My G...'

'As it happens, I'm not,' Eden clung hard on to her temper to cut in. 'You're Sterne Parnell, of course. W...'

A glint she did not like came into his eyes as he cut her off this time and, his summing up done in a trice, he stated, 'So you and Morrisey are in this together!'

'What...?' she began, and realised that her mind was obviously not going along the same track as his. But, feeling that she was going on to the defensive, she did something about it. 'There's nothing to be *in*!' she told him tartly.

'Not much! You're after my ward's money the same way Morrisey is.' And while she saw red at that remark, he further charged, 'You'd got it all worked out, hadn't you? He could marry my ward, while you hung around in the background to share the spoils. You...'

Eden's hand flying through the air made him break off. It never found its target, though, for, even quicker than hers, his own hand came up to grab hold of her wrist.

'The truth hurt?' he queried disdainfully, and as Eden snatched her burning wrist out of his hold she discovered that somehow in the small exchange Sterne Parnell had crossed the threshold and was inside the flat!

About to order him out, she was side-tracked when she saw his eyes flick around the apartment. Only then did Eden realise how she must have grown used to her surroundings. She was sure that she didn't care a button what Camilla's guardian thought of the shabby, not to say grotesque flat, but beyond doubt she knew that he was not as oblivious to its awfulness as Camilla had been.

Which made it odd, when she was certain that she did not care for his opinion on anything, that she should find herself hurrying into speech.

'Thomas isn't in!' she stated suddenly, realising that Sterne Parnell might have invited himself in for the purposes of seeing for himself if Thomas was there.

'How long have you known him?' Sterne Parnell clipped, ignoring her statement and fixing his cold grey eyes on her brilliant blue ones.

'Over half my life,' Eden replied truthfully. She saw him frown and guessed from that frown that he wasn't in the business of being led up the garden path. 'To save you working it out,' she went on sharply, 'I'm twenty-two, and Thomas didn't kidnap me from the cradle. We're not lovers—he's my stepbrother.'

'Your—stepbrother,' he repeated slowly, his steady grey eyes taking in the cut of her thick white-blonde hair, which fell in a straight line and ended bluntly, without curl or curve, just below her chin.

'Sorry to disappoint you,' she purred insincerely. 'It must be quite galling to be proved wrong, but not only are Thomas and I *not* lovers but related by our parents' marriage—but neither of us is after Camilla's inheritance. As a matter of fact,' she pushed on quickly when she could see by his face that he was about to insert something fairly acid, 'when our parents died . . .' Suddenly, she faltered. It was the first time she had spoken of the parents' death to anyone other than Thomas or Mr Boswell, and unexpectedly, she couldn't go on.

'You were saying?' Sterne Parnell prompted, and as Eden surmounted her moment of weakness she saw from his sceptical expression that he was ready to believe that anything she said would be pure invention of the moment.

'Thomas doesn't need to marry for money,' she told him flatly, and did not falter this time when she told him, 'We were both left amply provided for.'

She had rather hoped that had put an end to his scepticism. Not a chance! She followed his eyes as they did another swift circuit of the broken-down furnishings in the sitting-room. But, when she was expecting to receive more evidence of his cynicism, she was jolted more by the fact that he had interpreted her reference to 'our parents' entirely the wrong way round!

'What ill-gotten gains your stepfather bequeathed you and his son doesn't appear to have been put to very good use,' he commented icily.

Eden recovered fast from realising that he thought it had been her mother who had married Thomas's father, and not the way it had been. But he had reminded her of how cruelly he had yesterday told Thomas the awful truth about his father, and she was then prepared to see Sterne Parnell in hell before she'd put him right.

'For your information,' she told him loftily, 'Thomas and I are merely borrowing this flat from a friend while we look round for something suitable to buy.' She ignored his expression, which clearly said he thought she was making it up as she went along, and she told him coldly, 'In my view, it would be the height of bad manners to repay our host's hospitality by throwing out his possessions and replacing them with ours.' She didn't care then whether he believed her or not. It was more than time she showed him the door anyway. 'I'll tell Thomas you were looking for him.' She remained civilised to hint that he had overstayed his welcome. Her civility was wasted.

'Morrisey can go to the devil!' he grated brusquely. 'My only interest is in finding my ward.'

'Camilla's—er—disappeared?' queried Eden, but when Sterne Parnell stilled briefly, she rather gathered that he had seen straight through her innocent look. 'I haven't seen or heard from her,' she declared quickly—and truthfully. 'I've been out for hours,' she told him, 'looking at a property which I might or might not buy,' she inserted sweetly. 'So if Camilla's been here...' As she became aware that he was still watching her carefully, her voice tailed off. But curiosity quickly loosened her tongue. 'Haven't you been to your office today?' she queried.

'What the hell's that got to do with anything?' he barked unpleasantly.

Eden was getting a little fed up with one Sterne-uninvited-Parnell. She managed to remain even-tempered, however, as she remarked, again sweetly, 'I merely thought that you couldn't have been to your office, or you wouldn't know until you went home this evening that Camilla has—er—done a runner.'

Eden weathered the withering look he threw her and stayed calm while, tersely, he explained, 'My housekeeper rang my office when she came across a note addressed to me on my ward's dressing-table.'

'Such loyalty!' Eden scoffed.

'It's not a question of loyalty. It's a question of wanting what's best for Camilla.'

'You've told your housekeeper that my stepbrother's not good enough for your ward?' Eden erupted, her calm quickly fleeing at the very idea.

'I didn't have to tell her anything...'

'Because she, and probably your whole household, overheard you and Camilla having one almighty row!' she chopped him off, and then wished she hadn't.

'Given that my ward was more hysterical than articulate when I acquainted her with a few facts about Morrisey, I suppose the discussion we had could be termed an almighty row. But,' he said, his eyes fixed steadily on hers, 'if you've seen and heard nothing of her today, how is it you know that she and I have had a disagreement?'

'I...' Eden began, and for all of two seconds, she searched for some explanation. Suddenly, though, she wondered why she should bother explaining anything. 'I'm not on trial,' she said stiffly, and was on her way to the door when she told him sharply, 'If you don't mind, Mr Parnell, I'm sure you, like me, have a dozen or more things you want to get on with.'

She caught his dark look as she turned, and she knew that he had never been thrown out of anywhere in his life. To her chagrin, though, he made no move to join her by the door, and she realised that he had no intention of being thrown out now. She stared with hostility at the tall, athletic build of him, and knew she would come off second-best if she made an attempt to push him out of the flat.

With difficulty, she controlled her rising ire, but it was bluntly that she told him, 'I should like you to leave.'

'You can't want that any more than I want it myself,' he replied arrogantly. 'But since my ward has obviously been here today, and must now be out somewhere with Morrisey, I'm left with no alternative but to wait for their return.'

Eden came away from the door and wondered if her chances of hitting him had gone up at all. The determined look on his fairly good-looking face told her that, though he might think the flat only marginally better than a slum, if he had to, he would stay encamped overnight!

Sighing deeply, she did a quick mental recap on the letter she had found waiting for her. Then, sure that there was nothing there that could put him on to Thomas's trail, she asked belligerently, 'What did *your* note say?'

She had to give him top marks for being quick on the uptake. Without so much as a blink, he at once retorted, 'Short and to the point, Camilla wrote a defiant "I'm going to marry Thomas" and left it at that.' Eden was on the way to hoping that Camilla would be able to make Thomas see that the stigma of his father's crimes should not be allowed to prevent their marriage, when Sterne Parnell, nobody's fool, was bouncing back at her, 'What did *your* note say?'

For the craziest moment, Eden had the ridiculous urge to laugh. It wasn't funny, she told herself severely, and concentrated on trying to remember where she had put Thomas's note. She spotted a corner of it peeping out from under her handbag, and she moved towards the table. Extracting it, she handed it to Sterne Parnell.

It did not take him long to read it, and it was plain as he pushed the note back at her that he was not too thrilled by what he had read.

'What are you going to do?' she asked when, without so much as a thank you, he went striding to the door.

'I'll think of something,' he tossed over his shoulder, and without another word, he was gone.

Strangely, Eden's perverse sense of humour made her mouth curve upwards at his remark. Firmly, she shut the door after him. But she discovered, through what was left of that day, that she could not so easily shut him out of her mind.

Which, she decided when she went to bed, was not really so surprising. Without being conceited, she knew that she had her fair share of good looks. And to date, her experience of the opposite sex was that they were more prone to be warm and friendly to her than cold and hostile—the way he had been!

She got out of bed the next morning wondering how long it would take Thomas and Camilla to get themselves sorted out. Thinking that it might not take them very long to realise that nothing else had any consequence but their love for each other, Eden anticipated that Thomas might well telephone her that day.

For that reason she was afraid to leave the flat. Of a certainty, Murphy's law would come into being the moment she slipped down the road for a paper, and Thomas would choose that precise time to phone.

Thomas did not phone. Eden never left the flat for a moment that Wednesday, but not once did the phone ring. She did, though, have a visitor. A visitor she could have done without. It was some time after seven when a firm knock on the door of the flat saw her going to answer it. Instantly, her body impulses got ready for trouble.

How long she stood staring, unsmiling, at the tall, dark-haired man who stood silently looking down at her, Eden did not know. But when he seemed more waiting to be invited in than prepared to state his business, she found herself standing back from the door to allow him over the threshold.

'Has your stepbrother contacted you?' he asked crisply.

'No,' she said shortly, and was irritated with him and with herself for yielding to his unspoken demand to be invited in. She was irritated even more when she saw his eyes scan the flat as if seeking to see any difference from the way it had been yesterday. Suddenly she realised why he had called—Sterne Parnell was looking for some sign of either Camilla or Thomas!

His confirming, 'Neither he nor my ward have been here today?' sent her anger up another notch.

'What?' she exclaimed sarcastically. 'Don't tell me that your firm of private detectives has failed to pick up their scent!'

She saw it register that she knew about the detectives, but as he spared her a look of dislike in payment for her sarcasm, it was obvious that he had no intention of apologising for his actions.

'I dispensed with their services when, within a very short space of time, they were able to tell me all I needed to know,' he told her in a hostile tone.

Eden swallowed down the retort that it was a pity he had dispensed with the enquiry agents' service so soon. Had he not done so he might now be in receipt of the information that Thomas had inherited none of his con-man father's traits, and that soon he would have substantial funds of his own, which were in no way tainted by his father's criminal activities. But, because she was not sure if Thomas would want her to tell him anything,

Eden held her tongue on that issue. Instead, she looked up at him from beneath her long lashes, and told him with sarcastic sweetness, 'What a pity you've had a wasted journey!' She ignored the tough glint that came to his eyes, and syruped on, 'Neither Camilla nor Thomas have been here—I'm so sorry.' She tossed in a smile, and went further. 'If there's any message you'd like me to pass on—er—should they ring, I...'

'The only message I'm receiving at the moment,' Sterne Parnell broke in angrily, 'is one of a not-to-be-denied instinct to up-end you and paddle your insolent rear end!'

Eden knew she had pushed him too far, and the flame she saw in what she had thought were permanently cold grey eyes was sufficient for her to step back a couple of steps.

'You lay one finger on me,' she said, finding enough courage to limit her retreat to those couple of steps, 'and I'll sue you for...'

'Assault and battery, and no doubt colossal financial damages, as well,' he sliced in acidly.

It took her but a moment to recover from realising that he really did have the opinion that she was 'on the make'. 'You're impossible!' she hurled at him. 'Don't come here again,' she added, and not risking going too close, she skirted round him and went and opened the door.

Sterne Parnell took his time reaching the door. On his way he took out his pen, found a scrap of paper and wrote something down. He was still looking as though it would give him enormous pleasure to serve her with a good hiding, when at the door he stopped.

He was in control of his anger, however, when he passed the piece of paper over to her, and clipped, 'In the unlikely event of you being taken by a latent feeling of decency, perhaps you'll ring me if you see or hear anything of my seventeen-year-old ward.'

His words stung. Eden gathered he had meant them to. She masked her feelings by casting her eyes to the piece of paper he had given her. She saw he had written two sets of numbers—his home and his business, she assumed—and, having recovered, she raised eyes that clearly told him, 'Don't hold your breath', and smiled. 'I promise,' she said.

She saw she had angered him some more, but just as she was thinking she wouldn't have been too surprised if he'd stayed around to box her ears, to her relief, it appeared he thought that there was nothing more to be said. Without a word of goodnight, he abruptly departed.

Again Eden had to make a determined effort not to think about Sterne Parnell. She added arrogant, rude, and in sore need of a punch on the jaw to the label of cold and hostile person she had already given him. She then decided that he just wasn't worth wasting another thought upon. Just the same, she found he was again in her mind the following afternoon.

Having been certain that Sterne Parnell deserved to worry about his ward, Eden suddenly discovered that his reminder that Camilla was only seventeen had got to her. It must be an awesome task to be a guardian to a seventeen-year-old, she found herself thinking, and she started to feel quite in sympathy with him. That was, until she remembered the dreadful shock he had given Thomas. She was then back to being quite happy if Camilla's guardian went white-haired with worry—and, come to think of it, there had been a touch of silver at his temples. Eden promptly ejected Sterne Parnell from her thoughts.

With the exception of popping out to the corner shop for a loaf of bread, Eden had stayed, without result, near to the phone all day. When at seven-thirty that night it shrilled for the first time, she fairly launched herself at it.

'Hello!' she said breathlessly, and had no idea how expectant her breathless greeting had been until Sterne Parnell said loftily,

'You haven't heard from Morrisey, I gather!'

Her disappointment was total, and all Eden wanted was for him to get off the line in case Thomas was at this very moment trying to get through.

'Had I done so,' she told him, quite nastily, she had to admit, 'then for sure I'd have had the decency to ring you!' With that, she slammed down the phone. Fuming, she guessed that, since they weren't in the book, Sterne Parnell had either read the phone number off the dial when he'd been in the flat, or he'd been taking another peep at Thomas's personnel file.

Friday dawned, a miserable, cold, wet and windy day, and had Eden had anything she had to go out for, she would have thought twice about it. Thomas hadn't phoned yet, but he would know she would be anxious about him. Eden's knowledge of Thomas told her that, whether he and Camilla had sorted out what they had to sort out or not, if he didn't come back to the flat today, then she could be sure he would phone.

When seven o'clock that evening came with neither sight of Thomas nor a phone call, Eden started to wonder if she knew her uncomplicated stepbrother as well as she thought she did.

When, just before eight, the phone rang, she flew to answer it. She remembered, though, how her eagerness in answering the phone last night had been disappointed to find Sterne Parnell on the other end, and she hesitated. She counted three, and then, cautiously, picked up the receiver. She had to wait for the coin box pips to stop before she heard Thomas's voice.

'Thomas!' she cried. 'Oh, love, I've been so... Are you all right?'

'Fine. We're both fine,' he assured her, and went on to say that when he and Camilla had bolted, they had gone to the Lake District, and that they were renting a holiday cottage.

'A holiday cottage?' Eden repeated.

'Just in case Camilla's guardian makes her a ward of the court, we're in hiding and keeping well away from hotels,' Thomas explained, and broke off to ask, 'Have you seen anything of him, by the way?'

'He called here, as you thought he would, but he's no problem,' she quickly eased her stepbrother's mind.

'Good,' he replied, and went on to tell her, 'Luckily it's the end of the holiday season, so we had no trouble renting the cottage for a month. The only thing is, though,' he said, sounding a shade worried, 'although I stopped off at the bank and withdrew a tidy sum before we left, I paid the month's rent in cash, and now I'm all but broke.'

'You forgot to take your cheque book?'

'No, I've got that with me, as Camilla has hers. But, thinking about it, we've realised that any cheque we cash might easily be traced back to this area.'

'Could Sterne Parnell do that!' Eden exclaimed.

'There's nothing to stop him!' Thomas declared. 'He didn't hesitate to call in the private investigators before, remember. And since my salary was paid straight into the bank, his firm has a record of my bank account number.'

'Oh, love!' gasped Eden, and because that wasn't much help, she was at once practical. 'What can I do to help?' she asked.

Thomas fed more money into the coin box and asked her if she could deliver some food and some cash. 'Mainly food,' he said. 'Because we're afraid of being spotted, we're staying indoors during the hours of daylight.' He went on to give her the address, and said he'd be glad to see her as soon as she could make it.

'I'll start out straight away,' she told him on impulse, and was glad she had when Thomas exclaimed in a pleased way,

'Oh, would you!'

'Of course,' she answered, and she was practical again. 'Do you need anything else?'

'Since you mention it,' said Thomas, 'I, like Camilla, left home with very little in the way of a change of clothes.'

'Leave it with me,' said Eden, and a few minutes later, she had put down the phone and was hunting up the largest of their suitcases.

Hurriedly she packed extra clothes for Thomas, and since Camilla was, if shorter, near enough the same size, she packed some of her own clothes for her. Next she packed an overnight bag for herself, and then she went to clear out the food cupboard.

It had taken longer than she had thought to get everything together, and she placed everything by the flat door while she went to study a road map.

She hurried back and surveyed the luggage by the door. It amounted to two large suitcases, a shopping basket and two plastic containers of food, plus her overnight bag.

Realising that it would need two trips down to the car, Eden went to take up the first of the cases when she was suddenly pulled by the oddest notion. All at once she was overcome by the feeling that she should ring Sterne Parnell to tell him that she had heard from Thomas!

She blinked and a second later she was amazed that her insincere promise to let him know if she heard anything of his ward should have arrived to trip her up.

Strangely, though, Sterne Parnell was still in her head as she carried the first half of the luggage down the stairs. She remembered too her own unease until she had heard from Thomas, and she couldn't stop the feeling that Sterne Parnell must be going spare with worry over his missing ward.

Depositing her cargo in the ground-floor hall, Eden went back up the stairs to secure the flat and to collect the remainder of the luggage.

She had firmly decided that, after what he had done to Thomas, Sterne Parnell fully deserved to be worried out of his mind, but in taking a last look round, her eyes, as if drawn by some magnet, came to rest on the phone.

Blow him, she thought, and would have turned away. But, the irritating voice of conscience reminded her, insincere or not, a promise was a promise. When conscience further prodded—what harm would it do to ring him?—she could not see that it would do any harm at all.

She decided, however, that she would only ring him if, in the next sixty seconds, she could find that scrap of paper with his telephone numbers on it. Her eyes caught a vase-type ornament which she had bought to cheer the place up. Inside thirty seconds she had extracted the scrap of paper which she had carelessly dropped into it.

Half hoping that since it was Friday that he might be out painting the town, Eden picked up the phone and dialled. But, as though to endorse that he was too worried about his ward to contemplate being anywhere but near a phone, her call was answered straight away.

Taken aback, as much by her sympathetic thoughts as by the phone being answered before she was ready, Eden said the first name to come into her head. 'Sterne,' she said, and was about to swiftly change it and call him Mr Parnell, when he surprised her by recognising her voice.

'Eden!' he said sharply.

'Yes,' she answered, and realised that he was not being friendly, it was just that he did not know her surname. 'Thomas has telephoned,' she said quickly.

'You kept your promise!' He seemed surprised.

'I wasn't going to,' she admitted. 'Only—well, anyway, I though you might like to know that Camilla is fine.'

'Where is she?'

'I'm sorry, I can't tell you that,' Eden replied. 'Goodbye,' she added, and quietly put down the phone.

Hurriedly she secured the flat, and hastened with the remainder of the luggage to the carrying compartment of her car. Locking the rear door of her Metro, she went round to the side which up until then had been blind to her.

'Oh, no!' she cried, appalled, and not wanting to believe the evidence of her eyes. In the time elapsing between the last time she had used her car, Tuesday, and now, the tyre she had suspected of having a slow puncture had become as flat as a pancake!

Railing against fate, she realised that if she had not been so concerned about waiting in for Thomas to phone, she might have remembered to have that tyre checked over. As it was, she was the least mechanically-minded person she knew, and she was sure she didn't stand a chance of getting a mechanic to come out at this time of night to change the wheel for her.

Recalling how she had told Thomas that she would start out straight away, she stared helplessly at the offending tyre for all of two minutes. Another minute went by as she wished she had thought to take his phone number. But, remembering that he had phoned from a coin box, she realised that Begonia Cottage must be without a telephone.

She was in the middle of wondering how easy, or difficult, it was to change a wheel, when the most horrifying thought of all suddenly struck. It must be going on for fifteen minutes now since she had phoned Sterne Parnell. Why, oh, why had she done that! She had refused to tell him where Camilla and Thomas were, but what was there to stop him calling to try to make her change her mind! Knowing him, Eden realised that there was nothing to stop him! Speedily she went into action.

She extracted all the luggage and stacked it on the pavement believing as she did that since she probably had to jack the car up or something, a luggageless car might not be so heavy. She then inspected the mysteries of the tool kit.

The light in which she worked was not good. Fifteen minutes later, with nothing to show but a broken nail, Eden was tempted to go back to the flat and to wait for Sterne Parnell to pay a call. Once she had got rid of him, she could come back. Surely, if she was without the anxiety of expecting him to appear at any moment, she would be able to change the wheel in no time? Against that, though, was the thought—would Sterne Parnell be so easy to get rid of? Until she'd shown him Thomas's note, he had been prepared to wait in the flat for as long as it took for Camilla and Thomas to return.

Eden got on with the job of changing the wheel and wondered what she was getting worked up about anyway. Sterne Parnell probably had a late-starting date, and was even now escorting some female to a nightclub. Besides, it was pointless to go back up to the flat and waste precious time when it had never been his intention to pay the grotty flat another call anyway.

Eden had just convinced herself that she could forget about Sterne Parnell when she heard a car purr to a halt. Apprehension prickled down her spine. Cars in this neighbourhood did not purr! Cars in the area where Charlie Oakes had his flat coughed and spluttered, but never, ever purred. Car doors in this area crashed to. The car door she had just heard close had had a streamlined sound to it!

Eden renewed her struggle to separate what seemed a welded-on nut from its moorings. She heard the sound of footsteps, but she kept her head bent. The footsteps came near, and yet nearer, and then—stopped. She looked down at a pair of male shoes. Hand-made leather shoes, too, were very definitely alien to this area.

Eden knew that her worst fears were justified when she recognised the voice of their occupier. 'You appear,' he drawled, 'to be having a spot of trouble.'

CHAPTER THREE

EDEN was as furious with herself as she was with Sterne Parnell. Oh *why* had she telephoned him? 'If you were anything of a man,' she snapped, 'you'd offer to change the wheel for me!'

In contrast to her heat, though, she could hear no anger in him, only mockery, as he drawled, 'My, my, whatever happened to the emancipated female?' Eden did not deign to answer. She had just renewed her assault on the wretched immovable nut, however, when, 'Out of the way,' he said, and the next thing she knew was that a pair of strong hands had taken a grip of her tiny waist and—she being not swift enough to obey his orders, apparently—he lifted her 'out of the way'.

She could not truthfully have said that she had any objection to someone else changing the wheel for her. What she did object to was the fact that where, her nails ruined, she had found the wheel entirely immovable, Sterne Parnell had it removed in no time flat!

For a brief while she watched as he effortlessly secured the spare wheel in place. Peeved, she ceased watching him and went to stand on the pavement, where she mutinied against men in general and formed the opinion that it wasn't her role in life to know how to change a wheel!

Too late she realised that instead of mutinying, she should have been using her energies in thinking up some plausible story. For, much before she was ready, Sterne Parnell had joined her, and was commenting, 'I'd advise having the wheel I've just removed put right before you set out on your long journey.'

'Who says I'm going on a long journey?' she bit, before she had time to think.

For an answer, he pointed to the mountain of luggage which stood not too far away. Stifling a groan, Eden cursed her luck that she hadn't hidden the luggage away. There was nothing for it, though, but to try and brazen it out. At all costs he must be prevented from knowing where she was going, and why she needed so much luggage.

'Good heavens!' she scoffed, going round to the back of the car. 'One doesn't have to save one's luggage for long journeys only.'

Sterne Parnell helped her to re-load, but Eden made sure that she was the one who handled the food carriers. She had enough to be going on with, without having to think up some fresh explanation should a tomato or a tin of corned beef catch his eye. Grateful to close the rear door with nothing untoward happening, she grabbed up her shoulder bag, turned to him, and was ready with a dismissive but pleasant 'Thank you' when he got in first.

'Do I gather from that remark that you intend to go on a short journey, but for some length of time?' he queried.

From choice Eden would willingly have left him to gather whatever he fancied. But because of Thomas and Camilla, her choice was limited. For their sakes, she had to play it cagey.

'Mm,' she nodded, and moved a step in the direction of the driver's door.

'You're not worried that Morrisey might ring again?' Sterne Parnell blocked her path.

'No, not at all,' Eden told him brightly. 'Actually,' she added, counting ten and wondering about the pugilistic tendencies this man had awakened in her. 'Thomas knows I'm going to stay with a friend. It's a long-standing arrangement,' she smiled. 'Now that Thomas has phoned and I know that he, and Camilla of course, are all right, I can join my friend without worrying about him.'

'You're off to see some male friend?' Sterne Parnell questioned harshly, all mockery suddenly gone.

Eden looked at him in some surprise, but, when she might well have asked what he thought it had to do with him, she decided not to say anything that might delay her getting behind the steering wheel of her car.

'Not unless—Megan—has changed a great deal since last I saw her,' she smiled, and moved past him. She had her hand on the driver's door, when his voice arrested her.

'Before you go, Eden,' he said silkily, 'do you think I might wash my hands?'

Her own hands were filthy, but she was so anxious to get away that she had been prepared to overlook the state of them. Belatedly she remembered that she had not even thanked him for changing the wheel for her. She did not thank him then, but sent him a hostile look.

Without a word she led the way up to the attic flat. 'The bathroom's through there,' she told him as evenly as she could and went into the kitchen. Had she convinced him that she was on her way to stay with a friend, or did he suspect the truth—that she was on her way to Thomas and Camilla?

'Filthy' was understating the condition of her hands, but as Eden scrubbed them at the kitchen sink, she became agitated that Sterne Parnell might have seen through her every lie.

For a short while she contemplated putting off her departure until tomorrow. There were two things against that, though. One, Thomas and Camilla were expecting her to arrive tonight—even if the way the time was going, it would be early morning before she made it to the Lake District. The other fly in the ointment was that if Sterne Parnell did in fact suspect what she was up to, then without question he was going to have private detectives outside the flat by first light, all set to follow every move she made.

Eden found a nail file and realised as she tackled her nails that she just had to go tonight. No way was she going to lead any private detective straight to Thomas and Camilla.

The longer Sterne Parnell stayed in the bathroom scrubbing at his hands, the more Eden suspected he had not been taken in by her story that she was about to visit a girl friend. Thinking of their underlying dislike of each other, she was sure that in other circumstances he would by far have preferred to wait until he got home rather than avail himself of her soap and water. So his expressed wish to wash his hands, she realised, just had to stem from some whim to delay her!

Eden had all her nails filed down to the size of the one she had broken, and had left the kitchen by the time he appeared. 'Can't say that I care too much for the perfumed soap,' he murmured as he strolled towards her.

'My apologies,' she retorted, having grown too uptight to pretend. 'Had I know you were going to stake a claim on the bathroom, I'd have got some carbolic in.'

She saw the corners of his mouth twitch, as if he was having the hardest work in the world not to laugh. For some odd reason, her lips wanted to twitch too. She was glad she kept her wayward sense of humour under control, though, when, making it sound as if he was not more than passingly curious, he inspected his right hand for a hint of left in grime and asked casually, 'What, precisely, did your stepbrother say when he rang?'

The question, if casually put, was unexpected. Unexpected, too, was the way Sterne Parnell suddenly lost interest in his hand, and jerked his head up to fix her with a pair of piercing grey eyes.

'He—d-didn't say very much at all.' Eden hastened to get herself together. 'He was calling from a phone box...' She broke off, wondering if she had slipped up by telling him that much—she couldn't see how though—and went on '...He said both he and Camilla were fine.' She had to look away when, unpractised in barefaced lying, she lied through her teeth to tell him, 'Thomas just had time to ask to be remembered to—Megan—and to wish me a happy stay with her in—Wales, South Wales,' she made up on the spur of the moment, wanting Sterne to think she was heading in any direction but north, 'and then the pips went and Thomas didn't have any more change.'

Leaving him to digest what she had just told him, she half turned to the door, but she still had him in her vision. There was definitely a sprinkling of silver at his temples. It suited him, she realised, as she realised also that to some women, though not to her of course, Sterne Parnell might be dangerously attractive.

'Perhaps I'd better have her phone number,' he suddenly suggested when her thoughts were so elsewhere that she had no idea what he was talking about.

'Who?' she asked.

'Megan,' he enlightened her.

Eden gave herself a quick mental shake. 'What on earth do you want her phone number for?' she hedged, but she could not avoid the feeling that he knew darn well that she had no friend by the name of Megan.

She was convinced of it when he smiled, an insincere smile, and drawled, 'I should like to be able to ring you in case you hear from Morrisey again. I assume he has your friend's phone number?'

'Oh, yes,' she replied, her smile about as sincere as his. 'But Megan and I have such a lot planned, it's doubtful if you'll ever find us in. Perhaps,' she told him pleasantly, 'it will be better if I ring you again.' Edging towards the door as she spoke, 'It'll save you a lot of trouble,' she added, and opened the door.

She decided that his bland, 'It would be no trouble,' did not warrant an answer, and as he followed her out, she locked the door, and together they went down the stairs.

Together they stood on the pavement. 'Thank you for changing my wheel for me,' she smiled prettily.

'What else would I do on a Friday night?' he queried.

'What else indeed?' Eden murmured, casting an eye on his long, sleek Jaguar which was parked directly behind her Metro. 'Goodbye,' she said firmly, and went over to her car.

A surreptitious sideways glance as she unlocked her car showed that he was unlocking his. He raised a hand in a sketched salute and, silently damning him, she realised that he had seen her taking a crafty look at him. Eden waved an elegant hand back, and got into her vehicle.

It was her intention to 'see his car off the premises', and she fiddled about for an age without making any attempt to start the engine. When all of three minutes must have ticked away and he had not pulled out, passed her and gone on his way, Eden started to grow anxious.

Don't be silly, she told herself, but, compelled by Sterne Parnell to start her car or sit there all night, she turned the key in the ignition and switched on the headlights. The driver of the car behind did the same. Eden moved off; so did the car behind.

Her anxiety went up a notch when, although she was keeping her speed way down, the following speedy Jaguar stayed contentedly tucked in at the back of her.

Time and again as she headed out of London, she gave him ample opportunity to pass her. Other motor vehicles overtook the pair of them, but he never budged off her tail.

Eden took her eyes off her rear-view mirror when a sudden hazard meant that she had to give all her attention to what was happening in front. But, once she was clear of the hazard, she looked in her rear-view mirror, and her anxiety again rose. The Jaguar was still there!

For the next ten minutes she motored solemnly and sedately on. Suddenly then, her anxieties got to her. She didn't know for how long Sterne Parnell had it in mind to follow her, but she didn't want him still behind her when she reached the motorway. He'd know as soon as he saw her aiming for the M1 that she'd chosen a pretty odd route for South Wales.

Wondering what on earth time she might see Thomas and Camilla, Eden realised that she couldn't go anywhere near the M1 until she had shaken Camilla's guardian off. By luck, she had that very opportunity within the next few minutes.

Her car might not be as fast as his, but it was nippy. They were held up at traffic lights, and according to the lane she was in she should go straight on when the lights changed. But as the lights did change, she saw her chance, and she took it. Almost all in the same action, she checked that there was nothing in her path and putting her foot down, she spun the steering wheel to the left—and was away.

She was too busy concentrating on spinning round the next corner—a right turn here, and a left turn there—to have time to look in her rear-view mirror. For the next fifteen minutes Eden put everything she had learned about driving into practice.

Her heart was pounding and, as adrenalin pumped through her, she owned to feeling exhilarated when she pulled into the side of the road. She looked in her rear-view mirror, and looked around and about—and chuckled out loud. She had lost him!

Eden's exhilaration was such that it took some minutes for her to come down to earth a little. Then she took in her surroundings. Realising that she hadn't a clue where she was, she started up her car and set about finding a main road. A main road would have road signs, and they would give her an indication of where she was.

She had turned on to a main road, and had been travelling along it for some while before she saw a signpost looming up. She knew then that she must still be in the grip of exhilaration. Because while she realised from the signpost that she would have to make a right turn if she wanted to go in the direction of the MI, she just had to laugh out loud when she noticed that if she turned left, she would be heading for the M4—the motorway to South Wales!

Eden was still amused when she halted at the junction and indicated that she was going to turn right. She had no intention of going to South Wales!

The road was clear, and as she started to move off she checked her rear-view mirror—it was then that all her exhilaration promptly disappeared. Incredulous, she saw that the car behind was a Jaguar! Open-mouthed, she spotted that its driver was indicating that he too was going to turn right. Stunned, Eden acted automatically.

In a flash she had swung her steering wheel round to the left.

The swine, the cunning devil, the pig! she fumed as she started to recover. But no amount of name-calling would alter the fact that, although he had indicated that he would be turning right, Sterne Parnell had not done so.

Eden had still not finished fuming against him when the road which would give entry to the M4 loomed up. He was still right there behind her, and Eden realised that she had no option but to drive on to the motorway.

The belief that he would give up the hunt faded when the Jaguar tailed her on to the motorway. She hadn't really expected him to do that! She had thought, at the very most, that he might just follow her to see if she really was going where she had said she was going, and would turn away once he had seen her start down the motorway slip road.

On and on she drove, finding it most tedious to have Sterne Parnell right there behind, with her only crumb of comfort coming from the fact that he must be finding it even more tedious. For while other cars of the Jaguar's capacity were eating up the motorway in the fast lane, Sterne, since he had elected to dog her, was having to drive at the pace which she dictated.

She gave up hoping that he would leave the motorway at the next, and then the next, junction when, an hour later, he was still where he had always been. 'Drat him!' she muttered, and having realised that she stood no chance of seeing Thomas and Camilla that night, when the next turn-off point drew near, she made fresh plans.

As she fully expected, Sterne Parnell was right there with her when she drove off the motorway. She ignored him and motored around until she came upon a hotel.

She was not surprised when she parked her car to find that the Jaguar came and parked right next to her Metro.

Taking up her shoulder bag and her overnight bag, she left her car and continued to ignore Sterne Parnell. It was her intention never to speak to the odious man ever again.

She walked up to the hotel entrance, but as she stretched a hand out to the door, a firm masculine hand which had proved good at undoing wheel nuts was there to open the door for her. She continued to ignore its owner.

'You're a terrible driver,' he murmured with some charm as they entered the hotel.

Eden guessed he was referring to the merry dance she had led him around London, and to the fact that she had indicated right and turned left. But, with insult added to injury, she was hard put to it to keep her vow never to speak to him again. She bit down a string of heated words, and marched to the reception area.

It was then that she learned what it felt like to be ignored, for the male night receptionist-cum-night porter looked not at her, but at the man who had come in with her.

'Good evening, sir,' he said smartly.

'I'd like a room,' Sterne replied, and although she would not look at him, Eden knew that he was looking at her when he added, 'For one night only, I think.'

The receptionist was all attention, and Eden guessed wearily that Sterne Parnell was the type who would always have someone ready to jump to attention for him. 'Certainly, sir,' he replied. 'A double room?' he enquired.

It was Eden's turn to snap to attention. '*We*—are not together,' she told the man icily. She would have added that she required accommodation as far away as possible from the man who had just chanced to walk through the door at the same time when Sterne Parnell spoke. And in speaking, his very manner, in fact, gave the lie to anything but that they were normally the most intimate of friends.

'It would appear that I shall be sleeping on my own tonight,' he told the man behind the desk. Eden jerked her head round in amazement at the implication in his words, but only to have her amazement added to when, looking at the man she had known mainly as a terse brute, she saw that the very devil was dancing in his eyes!

Her hand sorely itched to knock that good-humoured look off his face but, having tried that once without success, she had no wish for a second disastrous attempt to be witnessed. As it was, she was sure the receptionist was convinced they had had a lovers' tiff.

At pains to let him know that she didn't even know the man by her side, Eden began, 'I'm sure this...' deliberately she hesitated '...gentleman—won't mind if you attend to me first. I'd like a single room, and I'm not sure for how long I shall require it.'

She maintained an aloof front as—new to the job, she imagined—he looked at the man he had thought was her companion, and seemed a trifle lost.

'Attend to my—er—the lady first,' Sterne instructed him, and had lost none of his good humour as he added, 'I'm sure she's most anxious to get to her room. Will you require anything to eat, Eden?' he asked attentively. 'I'm certain...'

'I'm quite capable of ordering anything I require, thank you very much, *Mr Parnell*,' Eden told him tartly, and could have bitten out her tongue. No way now was the receptionist going to believe that she didn't know the wretched man. Nor was he likely to think that they were barely acquainted, she discovered, for Sterne Parnell, enjoying himself hugely at her expense, could not resist taunting,

'Mr Parnell? We were on Christian name terms earlier this evening!'

She could not deny it, but she was ready to explode and she could see that if the receptionist was on anyone's side, then it was not hers. 'Do you have a single room?' she asked him sharply, her tone alone lodging him firmly in Sterne Parnell's camp.

'Certainly, madam,' he said, and was at his most efficient as he gave her a registration document to fill in.

Eden took the card and the pen from him, and wrote 'Miss E' and then hesitated. She was tired, she was not a little confused, and she was certainly a lot fed up, so it was no wonder to her that she couldn't decide whether it was wise for Sterne Parnell to know her surname or whether it wasn't. She wasn't even sure that it mattered. But she was aware that, despite his mocking exterior, he was nonetheless watching her every move. Eden hesitated no longer, and she dropped the 'Glendening' part of her name.

'Smith,' Sterne Parnell muttered over her shoulder. 'Now that *is* original!'

'How would you like a thick ear?' she spat aggressively, and hated him some more when all he did was to burst out laughing. She told the receptionist that she would find her own way when he handed her room key over, and without so much as a glance at Sterne Parnell, she headed for the lift.

She found the room she had been allocated without difficulty, but she did not immediately go to bed. She felt tired, she admitted that, and she had been through a whole gamut of emotions that night. She had experienced fear, anger, exhilaration and had felt the adrenalin soar through her veins. All wearing on the system, she realised, and enough to induce tiredness without the added trauma of having Sterne Parnell glued to her bumper all the way down the motorway.

She went to the bathroom and was getting washed and changed into her night things when she wondered—what about Sterne Parnell? Some time earlier she had pulled her head out of the sand to realise that he knew full well that she was making tracks to meet Thomas and Camilla. Yet, when if anything she would have thought he would be furious at the run-around she was giving him, he had not been angry at all! In actual fact, she recalled, he had seemed more amused than angry just now down in the foyer!

Remembering his amusement, though, and how he had implied to the receptionist—without so much as saying so—that they were lovers who had quarrelled, Eden thought it was about time she thought up something to make Sterne Parnell laugh on the other side of his face.

Before she climbed into bed she checked the hotel's reading matter, and wrote out a cheque for the cost of her night's lodgings. She decided that by now Sterne Parnell would be safely in his bed, and rang down and asked the receptionist for an alarm call.

'At three o'clock!' came his incredulous exclamation.

'That's correct,' she replied, and replaced the receiver to lie down and to make good use of the next few hours.

She was dead to the world when just after three her alarm call came through. 'Thank you,' she mumbled down the phone, and forced herself to get out of bed.

With the application of cold water to her face she came more awake, and the adrenalin started to flow again. This was where she outsmarted one Mr Sterne-Clever-Clogs-Parnell.

A short while later, and mindful of the other residents, Eden very quietly left her room. She took the lift to the reception area, but she could see no sign of anyone about. She placed the cheque she had made out, together with her room key, down upon the reception desk in passing.

She was grinning broadly as she left the hotel. Take that Mr Smart-Alec-Parnell, she thought happily. By the time you stir in the morning, I shall be miles away, and you'll never know in which direction I've gone.

At her car Eden placed her overnight bag down while she ferreted in her shoulder bag for her car keys. Finding them, she just couldn't resist a look back to the hotel.

A small laugh she couldn't hold in just had to be released. 'Love and kisses, Sterne,' she chuckled out loud. 'Are you in for a surprise!' she said gleefully, with nobody there to hear.

But there was somebody there to hear, and she very nearly dropped with the shock of it when, at a little after three in the morning, a voice she was getting to know very well said into the silence, 'Love and kisses to you too, sweetheart, but I'm afraid you'll have to be up much earlier in the morning to surprise me!'

Aghast, Eden spun round, and had no difficulty in making out the height, the build, and the face of her arch enemy. *'You!'* she gasped.

'In person,' he drawled, and was at his mocking worst when he challenged, 'Want to make something of it?'

To see her hopes—her certainty—of losing him go gurgling down the drain was deflating yet at the same time infuriating. 'Go to hell!' she erupted violently, and with her mind working as fast as her long legs, she grabbed up her overnight bag and went storming back to the hotel.

Damn him! Eden had been so delighted to have outsmarted him that she felt it as an affront that she had not outsmarted him at all. It was he, as ever, who had done the outsmarting. It was an outrage, and just too much to be borne!

Charging into the hotel, Eden snatched up her room key and the cheque which were just where she had left them. In the lift she angrily tore the cheque to shreds. There had to be some way of shaking off Sterne Parnell! There just had to be!

CHAPTER FOUR

EDEN overslept the next morning, and the fact did not surprise her. She reached for her watch, to realise that she had left it much too late to have another attempt at outwitting Sterne Parnell.

It was quite obvious that he had bribed the man who had been on duty last night to tell him when she left her room. That, or Sterne Parnell had told him some convincing tale. Either way, Sterne Parnell had been acquainted of her three o'clock alarm call, there was no disputing that. It went without saying, therefore, that some member of the daytime staff had been 'asked' to keep him aware of her movements.

Certain that if he was not lurking near, he would soon be alerted by someone that she had surfaced, Eden was in no hurry to see Camilla's awful guardian. Swine, she fumed against him, and stayed in bed until worry that Camilla and Thomas might be concerned that she had not turned up last night made her leave the covers to run a bath.

Dressed in the sweater and trousers which she had worn last night, Eden suddenly realised that she was starving hungry. Peculiarly, she saw neither sight nor sound of Sterne Parnell as she made her way to the hotel's restaurant. He was around somewhere just waiting, though, she was convinced of that.

'Am I too late for breakfast?' she asked a scurrying waitress on entering the restaurant.

'Not at all, madam,' the waitress replied, and showed her to a table.

Under the pretence of reading the breakfast card, Eden flicked her eyes to the one or two other late breakfasters. Sterne was not one of them, but since the restaurant was L-shaped, she didn't trust him not to be tucked away around the corner.

She tried to forget about the loathsome man as her order was brought to her. To forget him was difficult, though, and in consequence, she discovered that she was not so hungry as she had thought.

Her eyes watchful, she left the restaurant and decided that she would settle her bill before she went back to her room. She would not then have to worry about it if she saw some small chance of getting away without Sterne Parnell being any the wiser.

Eden had to wait while a receptionist attended to someone else, but as she waited in the foyer and looked all around, not so much as a sign of Sterne Parnell could she see.

Had he got tired of trying to guess what she was going to do next? she wondered. Had he, dared she hope, got fed up with the whole business and called it a day? Before any flicker of relief could arrive, though, Eden remembered his granite-hard, determined chin. Hope died. Once begun, she couldn't see him giving up on anything.

She tried to drum up hope again as she waited and idly observed as a middle-aged couple stepped out of the lift. Perhaps Sterne Parnell had an important appointment in London this morning! Perhaps it was an appointment that was so important that... Her wishful thinking abruptly ceased. For as her eyes followed the middle-aged couple out of the hotel, she spotted Sterne Parnell coming in.

He'd been out! All the time she had been dawdling about, getting bathed, messing about eating breakfast, he had been out!

She spared a moment to call herself a few uncomplimentary names that she had missed a golden opportunity, and a second later plan B was born. In an instant Eden had dashed to the lift and had leapt inside. As she pressed the button to her floor, excitement made her heart hammer as the lift doors began to close. She'd done it! He hadn't seen her! She could... Horror-struck, Eden saw a hand-made shoe suddenly appear and prevent the lift door from closing completely. She had seen that shoe before!

'Good morning, Eden,' Sterne said with some charm as with his assistance the doors parted to let him in.

Damn him, she fumed, and ignored his 'Good morning' to look to the various paper carriers and parcels which protruded from the new-looking holdall he had in one hand. Viciously she stabbed at the lift button again.

'Been shopping?' she queried sourly, and as the lift started to ascend, she wanted to hit the mocking smile off his face.

'Somehow or other,' he murmured, 'I appear to have come away without a change of linen.'

'How remiss,' she said tautly, and took another look at the holdall. By the look of it he had no intention of being caught out a second time. From what she could see of his purchases, if he had to follow her for a fortnight, he was prepared for it!

The lift stopped and she preceded him out of it. She had nothing she wanted to say to him, so she did not wait for him to accompany her, but went quickly along the carpeted corridor. He apparently had nothing he wanted to say to her either. Neither did he bother to catch her up—which was odd, she suddenly realised, because with his legs being longer than hers he could have made up the space between them in a couple of normal strides.

Abruptly she halted and looked back, to see precisely why Sterne had not caught up with her. He had not got out of the lift! Quickly she realised that his room must be on the floor above, or even the floor above that. Suddenly Eden saw a chance of her plan working!

Sprinting to her room, she stuffed her belongings into her overnight bag without a thought to neatness. She was ramming her arms into the sleeves of her car coat as she raced back to the lift.

She pressed the lift call button, but the lift was not there. Unable to wait, she raced for the stairs. Eden was not thinking of anything but escape when, her fingers in her shoulder bag seeking her car keys, she pelted out of the hotel.

She later realised that she must have been blind to everything but her purpose. Because although the fact registered that the Jaguar was parked next to her car, she was totally unaware that its owner was sitting inside and that he could, with the help of an adjusted rear-view mirror, observe every step of her approach.

Unlocking her Metro, Eden threw her overnight bag on to the passenger seat. Her shoulder bag had followed it, and she had a long length of left leg poised over the door sill when she had the shock of her life.

'You're surely not intending to skip without paying your hotel bill, are you, Miss—er—Smith?' asked a silky voice.

Speechless, she whirled round to see that Sterne Parnell had not gone on up to his room as she had assumed. The astute, abominable, detestable creature: instead of pressing the lift button to take him up, he had pressed the one for it to take him down again. As mad with herself as she was with him, Eden glared at him through the open window.

'Why don't you get lost?' she fairly hurled at him, her right hand starting to itch again.

'You know you'd miss me,' he mocked.

'Like a tooth abscess!' she slammed back, and didn't wait to hear another word.

She didn't thank him for his reminder that she had not paid her hotel bill, and she marched back to the hotel fuming, I hate him, I hate him, I hate him!

Eden settled her bill and decided that since Sterne Parnell was determined to shadow her wherever she went, she would set about seeing who got tired of the game first.

'Is there a cashpoint near here?' she asked the receptionist.

Armed with the information she required, Eden returned to her car, although this time she was very much aware that Sterne Parnell had her under observation.

Inside her car she referred to her book of road maps, studying it for quite some while. Then she started up her car. It was time to give Sterne Parnell the run-around.

She pulled out of the hotel car park knowing full well that she was going to turn right, but indicated to the Jaguar that was following that she was going to turn left.

She experienced a prickle of irritation that Sterne Parnell refused to be fooled again. For, on looking in her mirror to check which way he was signalling, she saw to her annoyance that this time he was more watching events than prepared to take any lead from her.

For once luck was with her in that, despite the town being full with Saturday morning shoppers, she managed to find a parking space near the cashpoint she was seeking. Her spirits lifted as she left her car. The Jaguar was a longer vehicle than hers, so Sterne just didn't have a chance of parking his car. The very least she expected was that he would have to double park. But, just as if the gods wouldn't have it any other way, she saw, unbelieving, that not one but two cars were moving out from the kerb. Smoothly, the Jaguar glided in and parked.

His luck's got to run out soon, she seethed, as she inserted her bank card and went through the motions of obtaining some ready cash. The sooner, she prayed, the better.

Solvent once more, Eden got back into her car, and started on plan C. Motoring out of the town, she saw a sign giving directions to the M4, but she ignored it. She still had every hope of losing Sterne Parnell before nightfall, but to her way of thinking she stood a much better chance of losing him if she opted for the twisting minor roads, rather than the more or less straight motorway. Eden pointed her car in a slightly northward direction, and set about giving Sterne Parnell the slip.

An hour later he was still where he had always been—right there in her rear-view mirror. She sighed, and grew more frustrated than ever. No amount of detouring down country lanes, or dawdling before putting on a spurt, could shake him. It had long since ceased to be a game.

She motored on, but she had not much idea of where she actually was until she saw a signpost for the M5. From her study of her road atlas she knew that the M5 went in a north and south direction. At once she realised that she had come much further north than she had intended.

Eden continued heading for the motorway, and wanted with all her heart to drive with the northbound traffic. But, with Sterne Parnell sticking like a leech, there was nothing for it but to take the southbound route.

As she drove on to the motorway and headed for Bristol, Eden found a few fresh uncomplimentary names for the man who did likewise. She guessed he would expect her to cross over the Severn Bridge at Bristol and head for South Wales. The way things were going, Eden could see herself doing that very thing!

She was in the middle of thinking that she had an idea how Sinbad felt to have the Old Man of the Sea on his shoulders, when something miraculous happened. She had earlier seen the sign saying that motorway services were up ahead, but she had paid no more attention than that. What did grab her attention, though, was that the next time she glanced in her rear-view mirror it was to see that Sterne Parnell was driving off to the service area!

Eden's brain was nothing if not sharp. Even as she put her foot down and accelerated into the fast lane, she had realised what had happened and was busy formulating plan D.

Quite clearly, Sterne Parnell was on the brink of running out of petrol, and must have reached a point where he had just had to pull off for a refill. Eden kept her right foot flat on the accelerator pedal as plan D was formed.

At the very next junction, she left the southbound flow of traffic. A detour and some minutes later, and she was again on the same motorway, but this time she was going in a northbound direction.

Eden felt more exhilaration as she and her trusty car sped north. Sterne Parnell's luck had finally run out—what a lovely day it was. Nothing could spoil her euphoria, not even when she saw the Jaguar coming towards her from the opposite direction.

She was driving fast in the outside lane going north, Sterne was driving fast in the outside lane going south. Their two lanes, with an intersection between, ran alongside each other, and as Eden had recognised the Jaguar and its driver, so she saw that Sterne had recognised the Metro and her. She saw that his expression was one of fury, and she was delighted.

But, having picked up exactly how he was feeling, she had less than a second to show him how *she* felt. Swiftly she took a hand off the steering wheel, and blew him a kiss.

Five minutes later she had sobered a little, but she was still feeling great. She had 'done him one in the eye', and it didn't matter that he must have twigged that her destination lay northwards. She was free of him. Free! Free! Free!

Eden's exultant feeling of freedom was not destined to last. She had lost count of time as she kept up a steady pace and wiped Sterne Parnell from her mind. She concentrated instead on Thomas and Camilla, and hoped with all her heart that Thomas would not prove stubborn on the subject of giving Camilla his name now that he knew of his father's prison record.

She remembered how much Thomas and Camilla loved each other, and she was on the point of thinking that nothing, not his father's past, nor Camilla's guardian, should stop them from marrying.

To conserve petrol she dropped her speed and switched to the slow lane. Then, to her horror, as if thinking of Camilla's guardian had conjured him up, she saw the long, sleek Jaguar breaking all the speed limits in the outside lane.

'Oh, no!' she cried, but she knew it was—oh, yes! By the time a service area had come into view, Sterne Parnell had dramatically dropped his speed and was neatly tucked in behind her. She indicated that she was going to the service area. To her surprise, he gave the same indication.

Deciding that she might as well break her journey now as later, Eden opted to go and have something to eat first and to fill up with petrol afterwards. She pretended she had not seen the Jaguar parked near as she left her car, just as she pretended that she had not seen its owner. She was not surprised when the owner followed her into the restaurant, though. What did surprise her, however, was that he should have the nerve to come and park himself at her table!

'It would appear that someone moved South Wales during the night,' he murmured, just in case she didn't know that she was heading in totally the wrong direction for South Wales.

'I know quite well where South Wales is!' She found him difficult to ignore.

'I see,' he said consideringly and, again to her surprise, he seemed to be much better-tempered about the run-around she had given him than she would have thought. 'Then I can only guess that you rang Megan before you set off this morning, only to be told that she would rather you met not in South Wales, but...' abruptly he looked up, and grey eyes were suddenly pinning hers when he asked quietly '...where, Eden?'

Hypnotised by his sincere-looking grey eyes, she opened her mouth, 'I...' she said, and shook her head, breaking out into a cold sweat. She had *nearly* told him! 'I think I'll have a salad,' she said, and looking from him, she fixed her eyes on nothing but the menu until the waitress came.

Eden was afterwards quite amazed at how unconstrained she had felt during the meal. It was most peculiar, she thought, that although she did not like him—and with him believing her to be a female with her eye to the main chance, he could not like her either—

the half-hour spent in each other's company had passed almost pleasantly!

They had been waiting for their food to arrive when she herself had started the conversational ball rolling. That in itself was odd, because the way things were, she should have been quite happy to go through the whole meal without saying a word to him. But she was discovering that love him—which she certainly did not—or hate him—which she did—Sterne Parnell was a man you could not ignore.

'So, how was your trip abroad?' she had asked, and had seen, even though much had happened since his return last Sunday, that he knew to what she was referring.

'From a business point of view, it went well,' he answered.

'That's good,' she murmured, but as their orders arrived, she found she had a curiosity in her nature about him. 'How did it go socially?' she asked, and added, 'I don't think you're married, are you?'

'From a social point of view, my trip went equally well,' he replied, not taking exception to her questioning, but answering her first question with a degree of charm, 'And no, Eden, I'm not married.'

It was on the tip of her tongue to ask if he had ever been in love, but she suddenly caught herself up short. Good grief, she wasn't the least bit interested in his love-life!

'Where,' she asked instead, 'did you go? While you were abroad, I mean.'

'The Far East,' he told her, and, questioned by Eden who had it in mind to pay Hong Kong a visit, but had not yet made it, he entertained her on the subjects of both Hong Kong and China throughout the meal.

She drank the last of her coffee and put her coffee cup down, suddenly realising that not one disharmonious word had passed between them. Giving herself a mental shake, she felt all at once totally disloyal to Thomas because she hadn't told Sterne Parnell to clear off the moment he had sat down at her table.

'Well,' she said, injecting a cold note into her voice, 'I must get on.' With that she got up and left the restaurant.

She had her car unlocked and was just about to get in when with horror she realised that she had not paid for her meal! Oh hell, Sterne Parnell would think she made a habit of it, and that she left a trail of unpaid bills wherever she went.

She passed him on her way back inside. 'Forget something?' he halted her.

'It must be your charm,' she offered sarcastically, 'I forgot to pay for my lunch.'

'I paid,' he said casually.

'I must . . .' she began, and dived in her bag for her purse.

'Bless my soul,' he mocked, to make her feel foolish as he eyed the people milling about, 'are you purposely trying to embarrass me?'

'Huh!' Eden scorned, and put her purse away and returned to her car. The person had not been born who could embarrass Sterne Parnell!

She was in her car and was driving near the Jaguar when she saw that he was waiting for her to pass before he pulled out. An imp of mischief promptly visited her, and she stopped her car, wound down her window, and waited until he had slid down his car window.

'You go on,' she told him, 'I've got to get some petrol.'

'Would I be so ungallant?' he replied.

She threw him a frustrated look and drove to the petrol pumps. She ignored him when, as insurance against being led another merry dance, she had no doubt, he stopped too, to top up the Jaguar's petrol tanks.

Aware that she was stuck with him for a while, Eden drove with due care and attention. The Jaguar was still behind her when she exchanged the M5 for the M6. By then she had put herself through the sternest criticism that she had actually sat and eaten her lunch with him. Not only that, but she had actually enjoyed the interlude!

It was his charm, of course. His phoney, put-on charm. She remembered how she had almost told him where Thomas and Camilla were. He'd spotted that, of course, because from that moment on he had put on the charm to get her relaxed when, unsuspecting, she might slip up and tell him what he wanted to know.

Remembering how unpleasant he had been the first time they had met, Eden had no doubts that there was underlying treachery behind his pleasantness. She was therefore doubly on her guard. Never again was she going to be lulled by his charm.

She was near Kendall, and as near to the address Thomas had given her as she dared to be, when she pulled off the motorway. With the Jaguar right where it had always been, Eden realised that since she dared not seek out Begonia Cottage, there was every possibility that she would have to book into a hotel again that night.

She recalled how, years ago, she, Thomas and the parents had stayed at a hotel overlooking Lake Windermere, and she motored towards Lake Windermere with her mind going into overdrive on the subject of outwitting her bloodhound.

She was busy with plan E, and was wondering at her chances of slipping out of the hotel and letting the air out of his tyres, when she spotted the hotel she was looking for.

Her assumption that Sterne would be booking into any hotel which she did proved correct. For when she turned into the hotel's car park, so did he. Eden left her car and went round to the rear to extract one of the large suitcases. It had been her intention to hand the case over for Camilla to borrow anything she fancied, but having worn the same sweater and trousers for two days now, Eden felt in need of a change.

Stern joined her at the door of the hotel. He had his new-looking holdall with him, and she guessed that the paper carriers and parcels she had seen had been thrust inside, for the holdall was now neatly zipped up.

'After you,' he said civilly.

'Too kind,' she grunted.

'Still Smith? he enquired as they approached reception.

'What?' she asked with mystified aggression.

'Are you still using the name "Smith"?' he enquired. She gave him a killing look, which had no effect whatsoever. 'How about Jones?' he suggested. And warming to his theme, 'Megan Jones has a nice ring to it, wouldn't you say?'

'Shut up!' Eden spat at him, and refused to blush that he was as good as calling her a liar over the non-existence of her friend 'Megan'. She stepped up to the reception desk and, determined to get in before this receptionist could make the same mistake as the one last night, she said, 'Good afternoon. I should like a single room.'

'How long will you be staying?' smiled the receptionist.

Eden smiled back. 'A week,' she lied unashamedly. 'Perhaps longer.'

While Eden filled in her registration card—mindful to book in as a single-barrelled 'Smith'—the receptionist attended to Sterne. Eavesdropping without conscience, she heard the same question asked of him: how long would he be staying? Certain that come Monday he would be hard at work in his London Office, Eden was not at all impressed that he was as big a liar as she was.

'A week at least,' she caught his reply.

The receptionist left him to complete his registration document, and returned to attend to her, where she efficiently summoned a porter to take her case to her room and enquired, 'Will you be dining in the hotel this evening, Miss Smith?'

Eden hadn't thought about it. 'Yes,' she said off the top of her head.

'I'll have a table reserved for you,' the receptionist smiled. 'What time would suit you?'

Again off the top of her head, 'Eight-thirty,' Eden told her, and without so much as a glance at Sterne Parnell she followed the porter to her first-floor room.

The room was light, airy, overlooked the lake, and brought back to Eden memories of happier times when the parents had been alive.

She made herself a cup of tea from the requisites provided, then went and ran a bath and realised that she felt down. She cheered up somewhat, though, when in the middle of having a lovely soak she had a splendid vision of an infuriated Sterne surveying four flat tyres.

The trick, however, was to first catch him napping. So far, he had proved very wily in that department!

Guessing that the hotel car park would be floodlit after dark, Eden realised that she was going to have to wait until after the hotel was quiet before she did her dastardly deed. At the same time as letting the air out of his tyres, though, she could get into her own car and be away.

When the time came for her to get dressed for dinner, Eden was feeling quite excited about her plan E. Sterne could not keep tabs on her all the time. But in the unlikely event of him keeping guard on the hotel entrance all night, there was always the fire escape.

Having looked at it all ways, the only snag she could see was her case. She could hardly scramble down the fire escape with it, nor could she walk past reception carrying it without questions being asked. The matter was resolved when she remembered that she had booked her room for a week. Her suitcase could stay here for a week. Once she was away from Sterne, she could go and buy anything that Camilla needed, and she could come back for her case and to settle up.

It was twenty-five-past eight when Eden checked her appearance in the full-length mirror. The midnight-blue dress was a particular favourite, but would in any case, she now realised, have been too long for Camilla. The very fine wool hugged discreetly to her slender but curvy figure and flared from the knee to end just below her calves. Eden felt good in the dress and remembered how she had been complimented the last time she had worn it.

She moved to the door and pulled it open, and found that she was face to face—with none other than Sterne Parnell!

'I was just about to knock,' he informed her, his expression unsmiling as his eyes travelled slowly over her face and figure.

Eden made hurried attempts to get over her surprise. But seeing him so unexpectedly like that, in fresh linen too, she observed, it took something of an effort for her to remember that she didn't like him.

'Why?' she asked as sharply as she could in the circumstances. 'Why were you about to knock?'

'I'm sure there was a reason,' he replied, giving every appearance of having forgotten what that reason was, 'but your beauty has taken it straight out of my head.'

'Goodbye, Mr Parnell,' she said coldly, certain that he knew a dozen or more beautiful women, and that he was much too alert for any one of them to cause him a moment's amnesia.

'I've just remembered,' he said, and had found a smile as he stood back while she stepped from her room and secured the door, 'I've come to take you down to dinner.'

Icily, she eyed him. 'Thank you all the same, but I can find my own way to the dining-room,' she told him shortly. 'Where...' she added pointedly, not forgetting his penchant for parking himself at her table, 'I...I have a table booked for *one*!'

She had started to walk along the corridor when he said, 'Two.'

Eden stood stock-still. '*What*,' she demanded frigidly, 'did you say?'

He looked not one whit uncomfortable, she observed, but was blandly pleasant when he answered casually, 'I overheard you reserve a table. I amended the reservation slightly.'

'You...!' His gall left her stuck for words.

'I knew you'd be pleased,' he said, and, taking a hold of her elbow, he propelled her forwards, remarking conversationally as they went, 'It's not much fun eating on your own, is it?'

'I should like the chance to find out!' she responded acidly, and said not another word until they reached a crowded dining-room, when she addressed the head waiter. 'You seem busy tonight,' she commented.

'Our chef has people booking up weeks in advance,' he replied, and sent her hopes of changing her reservation back again up in smoke by adding, 'I haven't one single table free this evening.'

'He couldn't have said that better if you'd bribed him to say it,' she hissed as the head waiter went on ahead to show them to their table.

'What on earth must you think of me!' Sterne replied, the picture of injured innocence.

'Don't tempt me,' she tossed back, but as she went in front of him, she suddenly realised that she was smiling.

By the time they were seated, her lips were under control and she had put the fact that Sterne Parnell had the oddest knack of reaching her sense of humour down to some peculiar quirk in her nature.

Eden selected independently from the menu, and Sterne left her to get on with it. Though he did consult her over the wine. 'Have you any preference?' he asked.

She shook her head. 'No,' she told him, and was of a mind to say nothing more to the man opposite.

'So,' he said, while they were waiting for the first course to arrive, 'tell me about Eden—Smith.'

It was there again—that charm. Eden was chary. It was on the tip of her tongue to tell him snappily that he could hire a private detective to tell him about Eden Smith. She cancelled the urge, deciding that it would be undignified.

'There's nothing to tell,' she said aloofly, but she couldn't see any good reason why she should be in the firing line, so she neatly upended his question, wrapped it up and lobbed it straight back at him. 'I'm sure you're far more interesting, Mr Parnell?'

'Sterne,' he invited, and added pleasantly, 'It wasn't my intention, when I changed your table booking, that you should be served a helping of boredom with your dinner.'

Clever swine, Eden thought, and, refusing to be put off, she dug her heels in. The arrival of their first course, however, made her hold back for a while, but no sooner had the waiter gone than she was remarking, 'You've been Camilla's guardian for six years, I believe?'

'True,' he replied briefly. But while his expression stayed bland, Eden did not miss the glint of ice in his eyes at her mention of his ward's name.

'You must have been rather young to be anyone's guardian,' she pressed on serenely, and began to enjoy herself at his expense, because it was for sure that he wanted to be the one who put all the questions.

'I was thirty-one when Camilla was orphaned,' he stated. 'She was at that time already at boarding school, so she presented no problem.'

'Until recently?' Eden suggested, and suddenly discovered when his brow started to come down that she didn't like it when he frowned.

'Until recently,' he confirmed, and had nothing to add.

Eden could think of nothing she wanted to ask, either, and they had started on their next course before she had recovered from the crazy notion that she cared whether Sterne Parnell frowned or smiled, or how he looked.

'Forgive my curiosity—Sterne,' she added as a sop in case he wasn't going to forgive it—not that she cared, 'but how *did* you come to be Camilla's guardian?'

'It's no great secret,' he shrugged. 'Her father was a friend who helped me when I started out in business. When Camilla's mother died in an accident, Alistair started to worry about what would happen to his daughter if some unforeseen accident happened to him too.'

'You told him not to worry, that—that you would look after her.'

'Of course,' Sterne said promptly, and Eden knew that he had not hesitated to give Camilla's father his word that he would act as her guardian.

'And when an accident did happen...'

'Alistair died as the result of a heart attack,' Sterne interrupted, and Eden was silent, her thoughts on the dreadful time that must have been for Camilla.

The impulse came to tell him that Thomas loved Camilla very much and would guard with his life against any ill befalling her, so that he need not worry about her. But Eden did not tell him anything of the sort. For one thing, she didn't know what decision, if any, Thomas and Camilla had come to about their future together. For another, she had a feeling that by reminding Sterne of his duty to his dead friend—not that he had ever looked like forgetting it—he would not be receptive to anything she said in her stepbrother's favour. Also, apart from the 'fortune-hunting' side of it, every instinct was telling her that while Stern had any say in it, he would never consent to his ward marrying the son of not only a proven confidence trickster, but a confidence trickster with a prison record.

Her thinking had caused her to grow edgy with him, and the bright blue eyes she raised to him were hostile when, her tone short, she said to Sterne, 'So, Camilla's father helped you when you started...'

Eden did not get to finish. Sterne Parnell, she gathered, had tired of answering her questions and had decided to put a few of his own. 'Alistair Rodgers put a lot of work my way,' he cut in to agree, and neatly upended the tables. 'Talking of work,' he said, 'what job do you do?'

'I intend to get a job,' she told him honestly, unable to see any reason not to. 'But at the moment I'm more concerned with finding somewhere decent to live than with looking for work.'

'You were telling the truth about borrowing that hideous flat while you looked for something to purchase?' he questioned, when she had been expecting him to say something pithy on the subject of her not having a job.

'Would I lie to you?' she asked wide-eyed, then laughter suddenly bubbled up inside her at her having lied her head off.

She was aware of Sterne watching her as her laughter escaped, and she saw his glance flick from her eyes to the merriment on her mouth. His glance was back on her eyes when she saw his lips start to curve.

She dabbed at her eyes and tried to control her amusement because, really, it wasn't all that funny. She thought she had control, but she was grinning idiotically when she agreed, 'You were right—it is a perfectly hideous flat, isn't it.'

Eden had more control of herself when the meal came to a close. She could not deny, though, that the atmosphere between her and Sterne had much improved.

'Would you like a liqueur to finish off with, Eden?' he asked.

'No, thanks,' she declined. 'The head waiter wasn't mistaken—the chef here's terrific. Another morsel of anything would be too much. I think,' she said, 'that I'll go to bed.'

Sterne did not stay down for a nightcap, but escorted her to her room. They had taken the stairs, and, her aggression nowhere to be seen, Eden actually found she was wishing that she had met him under other circumstances.

At her door he took her key from her hand, and opening her door, he looked down at her. For no reason, her heart started up a hurried pounding.

'Do you know,' he said softly, 'I could get to like you.'

'Steady!' she warned, and didn't know whether she was pleased, offended or what she was when his head came down and, gently, his mouth claimed hers.

'That,' he said as he straightened, 'is the one you promised me on the motorway.'

Eden remembered how she had blown Sterne a cheeky kiss as their two cars had passed, and she smiled up at him. When Sterne grinned back, though, she had the sudden feeling that everything was getting out of hand.

'Goodnight,' she said quickly, and reeled inside her room and closed the door.

How long she stood there all floaty and dreamy-eyed, Eden had no idea. Only as she undressed and hung the midnight-blue dress up on the outside of the wardrobe was she reminded of how she had originally packed that dress for Camilla to wear.

Abruptly Eden came to her senses. She had been determined that Sterne Parnell was never again going to lull her with his charm, but he had. Not that he had elicited any information from her of any importance, but that was not the point. By telling Thomas what he had about his father, he had hurt him. He did not want Thomas to marry Camilla, so therefore he had to be Thomas's enemy. And any enemy of Thomas had to be an enemy of hers.

Fifteen minutes later, Eden was changed into a fresh sweater and a clean pair of trousers. Her belongings were tidily packed, and she was whiling away the time until it was safe to put plan E into action.

Ten more minutes slowly ticked by, and she was contemplating making herself a cup of coffee to while away more time when a knock came to her door.

Thinking that someone from room service had come to the wrong room number, Eden went over and pulled the door back to see that the tall, dark-haired man who stood there was no staff member. Suddenly, though, as Sterne Parnell stared down at her, she realised that he could be forgiven for believing that if she was going to change into anything at this hour, it wouldn't be into the casual clothes she had on, but into her night attire!

That thought gave birth to another, and she swiftly dismissed any flicker of excitement that new thought brought, to attack hotly, 'If you've come to my room thinking to continue from that kiss . . .' Her voice trailed off. Only then did it register that Sterne's expression was more grave than amorous.

'Don't get your hopes in an uproar!' he barked curtly. 'There's been an accident. I've only come to tell you that your stepbrother's in hospital.'

CHAPTER FIVE

'THOMAS is in hospital!' Eden gasped, and was instantly a mass of suspicion, fear and apprehension. 'You—wouldn't—lie to me just to find out where they are, would . . .'

'Good God, woman!' rapped Sterne, and was so impatient with her that when he half turned she thought he was going to stride off without another word.

'Please!' she said urgently, and took a hurried hold of his arm to detain him. She let her hand fall when she saw that he had hung on to enough control to stay, and to detail,

'There was a car crash. Both Camilla and Morrisey are in hospital. Both—are in a bad way.'

Eden felt her knees buckle, and she groped for something to hang on to. But Sterne's reactions were immediate. No sooner did he observe how the stuffing seemed to have been ripped from her than his hands were there supporting her.

'No! Oh, no!' she moaned, and her mind was filled with the horror of hearing of another car crash—the one that had killed her parents.

Vaguely she became aware that Sterne had a firm grip of her upper arms and was leading her back inside her room and was making her sit down on the bed.

'I'm sorry,' she mumbled, making desperate attempts to rise above her shock. 'I don't usually—g-go to pieces,' she told him shakily, and tried to explain, in a rather incoherent fashion as it turned out, 'The parents—my father—they—he—was killed in a c-car crash.'

Striving for control, she took a few deep breaths. But only as her initial shock started to ebb did she remember that Sterne thought her father had died eleven years ago at least. Though quite when her father had died was immaterial, she realised.

'I w-want to go to Thomas,' she told Sterne, getting to her feet. 'Which hospital is he in?'

'You're in no state to drive,' Sterne pronounced. 'I'll take you.'

'I...' Suddenly, as she realised how remiss she had been, all protest faded. 'Of course,' she said, 'you're going to the hospital to see Camilla. I'm sorry, I never...' Her voice tailed off when Sterne, seeing the car coat which she had placed ready on the bed, took it up and held it out for her to put her arms in.

A numbed feeling took charge of her as she went with him to the car park. That numbed feeling persisted as he assisted her into his car and drove out of the hotel car park.

Sterne drove in silence, but Eden was so unaware of anything but what he had told her that he could have driven one mile or twenty miles before that silence started to get to her.

'How bad is he—are—are they both?' She just had to break that grim silence.

Her nails were digging into her palms, but she still felt the jolt when he replied tersely, 'Critical.'

'Both of them?'

'Both,' he answered, and a grim silence fell once again.

Eden prayed desperately that Thomas and Camilla would pull through. She willed them both to make it, but when reality tried to get a hold to tell her that they might not make it, she could not take that, and she broke into speech once more.

'How...' she began, but her voice was suddenly choked.

'How did it happen?' Sterne misread her question. 'From what I've been able to glean, they were out for a spin in some death-trap of a car when the already faulty brakes failed.'

As Eden absorbed what he had said, she did not miss the inflection of censure in his tone. 'The car isn't Thomas's,' she defended him quietly. 'We were going to go abroad, so he sold his car...'

'Obviously being more interested in a holiday abroad than in having a sound mode of transport,' Sterne cut in sharply.

Eden was about to tell him that she and Thomas had been going abroad to live, not for a holiday, when suddenly it seemed irrelevant. It seemed much more important just then to put the question she had meant to ask earlier. 'How...' she began instead '...do you know about the accident?'

'There's no mystery,' Sterne replied coldly. 'Since I didn't know where the hell you were leading me, it was impossible for me to leave a number where I could be contacted.'

She supposed that leading Sterne a wild-goose chase had had its amusing side, but it had ceased to be in any way funny. 'You wanted a point of contact in case Camilla got in touch?' she queried flatly.

He nodded. 'I rang my housekeeper last night but, as expected, Camilla hadn't phoned.'

'You rang your housekeeper again tonight?' Eden guessed. 'After dinner...' she realised, because, had it been before, she and Sterne would never have dined together and she would never have—enjoyed his company!

'I rang her after dinner,' he agreed, while Eden was batting away any idea that she had found his company pleasant.

'Camilla had again not been in touch?'

'She hadn't, but the police had.'

'To tell you of the accident?'

Again he nodded, and revealed, 'After ringing my housekeeper, I rang both the police and the hospital.'

'The hospital told you that Thomas and Camilla were both in a critical condition.' Eden wanted him to confirm.

'I wish it was otherwise, but it isn't,' he said, and Eden felt darn sure that it was only Camilla he was concerned about. He didn't give a damn whether Thomas lived or died.

'What did the police say?' she pushed out from between her teeth. 'And how did they know to get in touch with you—with your home?'

Her tone drew her a sideways look from Sterne, but it didn't appear to have bothered him as he answered, 'Camilla's cheque book and a letter with her address on it were in the bag she had with her.'

Eden accepted that it wouldn't take the police long to have Camilla documented, but... 'Do they know Thomas's name?' she asked quickly, having assumed that both Camilla and Thomas were too ill to tell them anything.

'They do now.'

'Because—you told them?' she guessed.

'I couldn't see any reason why I shouldn't,' Sterne replied curtly. 'If he'd stolen that car and in consequence had a good go at killing my ward, than as far as I'm concerned, he deserved everything that's coming...'

'He didn't steal the car! I've...'

'According to the police, the car's registered in one name, his cheque book in another, while the receipt in his wallet for rent on a cottage he's renting is in another name entirely.'

'You'd hardly expect him to use his real name only to have you standing on the doorstep before he and Camilla were able to get anything sorted out!' Eden snapped angrily.

'Sorted out!' Sterne bit. 'By God, he needs some sorting out!'

Eden checked the urge to physically hit out at him. Her feeling of numbness had disappeared completely and her fears for Thomas, together with Sterne Parnell's odious manner, were the cause of her wanting to lash out at the man by her side, she realised.

They drove the rest of the way in stony silence. When they entered the hospital forecourt, her anxiety for Thomas was such that she barely waited for the car to stop before she was out and was hurrying towards the entrance. Sterne too had moved quickly, she discovered, for he was there at the door to open it for her.

Once inside, it was he who took over. Eden had realised that the charm he had once treated her to was at an end now that he had the information he required—the whereabouts of his ward.

His innate sense of catching up with people hadn't faltered, she found, for they had soon caught up with the doctor who had attended the two accident victims. In no time flat, Sterne had stated who they were and was asking for the latest news.

'Things are not so good, I'm afraid,' Dr Henry replied, and went into detail about the extent of Thomas and Camilla's injuries.

'May I see my stepbrother?' Eden asked.

Dr Henry did not hesitate. 'Of course,' he said, 'for a few minutes,' and while Eden went in one direction, Sterne went in another.

Her heart was in her mouth when she entered the side ward where Thomas lay and she saw how festooned with tubing and piping he was. Dr Henry had seemed more concerned about Thomas's state of unconsciousness than the few not too serious internal injuries he had sustained, and as she looked down at his pale face, Eden was hard put to it to hold back tears.

Willing him to get better, she took a gentle hold of his hand as if hoping to transmit some of her will, some of her strength, to him.

When a nurse came in to monitor him, Eden realised that her few minutes with him were up, and she let go of his hand. She wanted to stay with him, but she in no way wanted to hinder the nursing staff if their efforts could make him better.

'Is—is he...' Eden began, but she just could not finish the question of whether he was going to pull through.

'We'll do our best,' the nurse said gently.

Eden left the side ward and went a few steps down a corridor without any real idea of where she was going. 'Are you all right?' asked a voice she knew.

She looked up and saw Sterne Parnell. 'I'm—as well as can be expected,' she said, without humour. 'How—about you?' she asked, observing at that moment that he seemed to have lost some of his colour.

'I can't abide hospitals,' he replied grimly. 'Let's get out of here.'

Everything seemed unreal to Eden when, entirely without protest, she went with him down and along corridors until they were outside the hospital. How real could it be? she pondered. Both Thomas and Camilla were critically ill and unconscious, yet she and Sterne had not asked after the two people they had just left, but he had asked 'Are you all right?'—just as if she looked as ashen as she felt, and she had asked 'How—about you?'

They had reached the Jaguar before any sort of reality came back to Eden. She was standing by the passenger door while he went round to the other side, when she enquired, 'Where were you thinking of going?'

Sterne looked at her over the roof of his vehicle. 'There's nothing we can do here but be in the way,' he said. She heard the car locks undo as he turned his key in the door, but his gaze was still on her face illuminated in the lighted area, when he added, 'We might as well return to the hotel, to get what rest we can.'

Wearily she checked her watch, and was shaken to find that it was only one o'clock in the morning. She felt drained and as if every minute of this crisis-time had taken an hour to pass. Suddenly though, despite her weariness of spirit, she felt a decided aversion to returning to the hotel.

She stepped back. 'I don't want to go back to the hotel,' she said and, certain that Sterne would return to the hotel on his own, she turned away from the car.

'Why?' his voice reached her.

Eden halted and felt that to say that she did not particularly enjoy staying in hotels would sound a stupid excuse. 'I—it's too far away from the hospital,' she replied, and saw that he was giving her answer due consideration.

'Maybe you're right,' he said, and felt in his jacket and then held a door key aloft. 'They found this in the pocket of Camilla's jeans when they cut them from her,' he informed her. 'If I'm not mistaken, it fits the door of Begonia Cottage. It's barely any distance from the hospital,' he stated, and added, as if it was settled, 'We'll go there.'

'You know about Begonia Cottage—the address!' Eden exclaimed as she played for time. She wasn't sure that she wanted to go to the cottage either.

'I've had the address of Begonia Cottage since I rang the police and was able to throw some light on the "Mr Jenkins" who was renting it.'

'Oh!' Eden said softly, as it dawned on her that 'Jenkins' was the alias that Thomas had used. 'But,' she began to protest, 'there's no phone at the cottage.'

Sterne's answer was to come round and open the passenger door for her. 'If the news gets worse, we'll soon hear about it,' he told her curtly, and ordered, 'Sit there, while I go and tell them where we'll be.'

Bossy swine, Eden thought wearily. His charm hadn't stayed around long once he'd found out all about Begonia Cottage, had it! He was soon back though, and it seemed to Eden that no sooner were they driving away from the hospital than they were pulling up at Begonia Cottage.

It was a small semi-detached dwelling, and the key which Sterne had in his possession did indeed fit the door lock. Their arrival at gone one in the morning, however, had not gone unnoticed.

Sterne had hardly pushed the door open when they both heard the sound of the adjoining cottage being unbolted. A stream of light lit the darkness as a woman with a topcoat over her nightdress opened the door and came out.

'I'm Mrs Fox,' she introduced herself. 'I'm the owner of these two properties,' she added a shade frostily.

Eden left it to Sterne to tell Mrs Fox who they were and what they were doing entering her property. It transpired that Mrs Fox had already had a visit from the police enquiring about Mr Jenkins and his companion, but she promptly lost her slightly frosty manner when Sterne told her who they were and that they had just come from the hospital.

'How are they?' she asked with gentle sympathy. 'Such a lovely couple, and...'

'We'll know more in the morning,' Sterne cut her off, apparently not interested in what a lovely couple his ward and the old lag's son were.

'Well, I'll hope the news is better in the morning,' Mrs Fox said, unoffended by his brusque manner in the circumstances. 'And you'll be nice and near to the hospital in Begonia Cottage. Now,' she said, starting to show her efficient side, 'let me go and find you some clean sheets, then you can get to bed.'

Eden let Sterne go with Mrs Fox. He was as capable as she was of collecting the sheets, she considered, as she entered the small hallway of Begonia Cottage. She felt along the wall for the light switch, and having found it she went on to discover a larger than anticipated pleasant sitting-room, and a quite large kitchen-cum-dining-room.

She left the kitchen and was stepping into the hall when Sterne, laden with sheets and towels, came in through the front door. She went up to him and extracted a pair of sheets and pillow cases, and helped herself to a towel from off the top of the pile he held.

'I'm for bed,' she said tonelessly. 'Goodnight.'

If he answered, she did not hear. She flicked on the light switch to the stairs and ascended. At the top of the stairs she was confronted by three doors. The first door was a bedroom, as was the second. The door at the far end, and opposite to the stair head, proved to be a tiny bathroom. Eden took the bedroom nearest the bathroom and suddenly had another fight against tears when she saw a tie she had given Thomas draped over the small dressing-table mirror.

Hastily she stripped the bed and remade it. She was in the bathroom having a wash when she realised that the only clothes she had with her were those she stood up in. Sterne's remark 'Somehow or other, I appear to have come away without a change of linen' came back to her, and she choked on a laugh that threatened to turn into a sob.

Once she had washed, Eden rinsed through her smalls and wrung them almost dry in the towel. She thought that Mrs Fox could have been forgiven had she come in to turn off the central heating once she knew that her tenants were in hospital. But she had not done so, and Eden was glad of that fact when, wrapped only in a damp towel, and with her damper smalls in one hand, she vacated the bathroom.

The way her luck was going it did not surprise her that Sterne should round the head of the stairs at the precise moment she left the bathroom.

She was determined not to look as flustered as she felt, but in the four steps it took her to get to her room she was aware with every step of his eyes on her naked shoulders and the long length of leg she was exposing.

The short, 'Goodnight,' she bade him arose from that flustered feeling, for she had already bidden him goodnight. This time, though, she did hear his reply.

'Goodnight,' he said coolly, and as she reached her bedroom door, he opened the other bedroom door and went in.

Putting her smalls to dry over the radiator, Eden removed her towel and put that to dry too. Then, there being nothing else for it, she got into bed, put out the light, and slept in her skin.

That was to say, she would have slept in her skin, had she been able to sleep. But no sooner had she put out the light than her fears for Thomas were magnified. On and off through the night she dozed when she could, but in her waking hours she found no peace, so that at one point she was hard put to it to stay where she was and not to get up and go charging to the hospital.

It was a very long night, and Eden felt she had only just fallen into another light doze when she was rudely awakened by someone coming into her room. It was a dark morning, and to add to his or her impudence, the intruder switched on the light.

Her reaction was to sit bolt upright before she was fully awake. 'Who...?' she questioned, and she was not sure for a second who she was, where she was, or who the tall dark-haired man was who had halted by the bed.

But he was not looking at her face, and her sleepy eyes followed to where his gaze had been drawn. It was then that any remnants of sleep abruptly departed. For, with a tremendous jolt, she saw that what held his gaze in some fascination was the sight of her left breast, the pink tip of which was peeping shyly over the bed sheet!

If Eden had been determined not to look flustered last night, then she discovered that having a man see her pure femininity on display gave her no chance to control anything—and that included her blushes.

'Get out!' she screamed, her control of her temper gone too, and as scarlet colour flushed her creamy complexion, she yanked the bed covers up to her chin.

'Good God!' Sterne exclaimed incredulously, his attention more on the fiery colour of her cheeks than on her fiery temper. 'You're not a...' He broke off, looked deeply into her brilliantly blue eyes and observing that her skin was still a geranium red, he altered what had started out as a question, to a statement. 'You are—you're a virgin!' he stated.

'What if I am?' snapped Eden, still very much confused but glad to feel her high colour fading. 'Or is that a crime too?' she challenged.

'It's no crime,' he recovered from his incredulity, 'it's just . . .'

'What?' she snapped.

'I'd assumed, since your eyes and mouth belie frigidity,' he shrugged, flicking his glance to her mouth and back to her eyes again, 'that a woman of your beauty and intelligence would have taken up at least a couple of the offers that must have poured in since you reached the age of consent.'

Her cheeks felt warm again, but she brutally ejected any small glow that Sterne thought she had beauty. As for her intelligence—she hadn't got rid of him yet, had she?

'At the risk of ruining your years of research, allow me to tell you that not every passable-looking, faintly intelligent female over the age of eighteen is a tramp,' she told him hotly, and while she was in the mood, 'Now clear off!'

He did not smile, but neither was he offended. 'Is that any way to thank me for your early morning tea?' he mocked, and turned to go back for the cup and saucer which he had placed outside the door while he found the light switch.

Eden gave him no thanks. 'Where did you get the milk?' she asked in a hostile tone. 'There was none in the kitchen last night!'

'It came with the sheets and towels,' he said, his eyes flicking to where her towel was draped near the radiator. Eden refused to colour again at his not being able to miss seeing her flimsy underwear either, and he had no comment to make on the subject as, observing the way she was still clutching the bedclothes to her, he drawled laconically, 'Rather than risk you letting go of your security blanket, I'll leave your tea on the bedside table.'

Eden ignored his mocking comment, and watched while he placed the cup and saucer near her. It was as he straightened, though, that her powers of observation awakened, and with them, some of the intelligence he had credited her with. Last night he had been as razorless as she had been nightdressless. Yet, when with his colouring he should by now be sporting a fine dark shadow on his chin, of shadow there was not a sign!

'You've shaved!' she accused. 'And you've changed your shirt!'

'If you want to get really personal, I've had a bath as well,' he mocked, but his mockery had gone, when, as he looked at the shadows beneath her eyes that told of her unhappy night, 'Like you, I couldn't sleep,' he owned. 'I returned to the hotel. I checked us both out.'

Eden was fairly astonished, since what sleep she had managed to get had only come in fits and starts, that she had not heard him leave, nor come back in. But, while she accepted that he must have gone about it very quietly so as not to disturb her, her intelligence told her that of course he would have brought his belongings back from the hotel when he checked out. But—what about hers?

'My case . . . ?' she began to ask.

'Funny thing,' he cut off mockingly, 'your case was all packed ready when I went to your room. Even your toothbrush was put away,' he murmured.

Eden gave him a speaking look, not doubting for a moment that within a second of seeing her packed luggage, he had known that she had planned to do a disappearing act.

'Did you bring my things?' she questioned shortly.

He nodded. 'I raided the carrying compartment of your car too.'

Eden still had the keys to her car in her bag. 'And you've got the cheek to think that *I* have criminal tendencies!' she couldn't resist throwing at him—when he might have been expecting her to thank him instead.

She saw his expression darken at the word 'criminal', and she just knew that he was renewing his belief that her stepbrother was making up to his ward from some criminal attempt to get his hands on her fortune.

'I'll bring your cases up,' he barked, and turned about.

'Leave them outside the door!' she ordered his departing back. The slam of the door told her that something had upset him.

She heard him coming back up the stairs. When, without a knock or a word, her door opened and her two large suitcases were placed inside the room, she realised she ought to have known that Sterne wasn't about to start taking orders from anyone.

A minute after he had gone she was at her luggage unearthing a housecoat to put on. That achieved, all she could think about was getting to a phone box to find out how Thomas was. Quickly she cleaned her teeth and washed, and hurried into a sweater and trousers.

Going back to her room, she checked her purse and saw that she did not have change for the phone box. Purse in hand, she ran down the stairs in search of Sterne.

She found him in the sitting-room. 'I want to phone the hospital. Can you change . . .' she began, only something in his expression caused her to break off.

'I've just phoned,' he informed her.

'What . . . ?' she asked, her voice suddenly husky, knowing from his expression that the news was not good. 'What—did the hospital say?' she made herself ask.

'Camilla is still fighting for her life.' He told her that which he considered the more important.

'And...' Eden's throat went dry, 'Thomas?' she croaked. She was stunned into silence when, unemotionally, Sterne told her:

'Morrisey—he's in a coma.'

For dazed seconds she stared at the impassive man who had just delivered the shocking news that her dear stepbrother was in a coma with about as much emotion as he would ask a news vendor for an evening paper. Her eyes were large in her face when Eden realised that Sterne Parnell would set out to charm the devil himself if it got him what he wanted. He had wanted to know the whereabouts of his ward and, in receipt of that information, he no longer had any use for Eden Smith, and cared not at all how the news he had just imparted affected her.

'Coma!' she repeated as shock released its grip. 'Thomas is in a coma!' she said faintly and, her voice gaining strength as she started to go out of control, she yelled at him, 'It's all your fault! If you hadn't interfered, Thomas and Camilla wouldn't have run away, and none of this would have happened! If...'

'If I hadn't interfered,' Sterne sliced in icily, 'my ward would by now be engaged to a man who I don't doubt is on the way to being as big a con-merchant as his father!'

Fury such as she had never known erupted in Eden. Her right hand flew through the air seemingly of its own volition. But her effort to serve Sterne Parnell a vicious blow for his awful comment was blocked when he anticipated her move and, as he had once before, caught hold of her wrist.

'You swine!' she hissed frustratedly. 'I hold you totally responsible for what has happened!' she hurled at him furiously. 'I-If Thomas doesn't—doesn't recover,' she said, white-faced and shaking in her shock and fury, 'I'll never forgive you!'

'If he does recover, and my ward does not,' Sterne told her grimly, as he threw her wrist from him, 'then *I*, personally, will make him wish that he hadn't!'

It was no idle threat, and Eden knew that it wasn't. Sterne Parnell meant every word of it. She sent him a look of loathing—it was returned with a bonus. There was nothing more to be said. She turned about and ran to her room where she scooped up her coat and her bag.

Pulling on her coat as she went, she ran back down the stairs and out of Begonia Cottage. She was in a desperate hurry to get to the hospital.

Wishing she had never left the hospital, Eden felt her anxiety for Thomas peak as she passed Sterne's car. Heartily did she want her car, but in the absence of transport she smartened her pace. It seemed vital to her that she reach the hospital with all speed.

Her worry over Thomas increased with every hastening footstep. When the Jaguar purred up to her and glided past her, she was certain that Sterne was clapping his hands that he had transport and she did not. Just as she was certain after their heated exchange a few minutes ago that he would cut his throat sooner than give her a lift.

In that, though, she was proved wrong. For a little way up the street, the Jaguar halted. It was then that her pride came under pressure. When she had left the cottage she had believed that wild horses would not get her inside the Jaguar again. But as she neared the car and saw Sterne lean over and open the passenger door, her urgent need to get to her injured and much loved stepbrother became more important than pride.

She knew as though it was fact that Sterne Parnell did not give a hoot whether she accepted a lift or whether she didn't. For certain he was not going to beg to be allowed to drive her to the hospital.

Eden drew level with the open passenger door. Pride was no longer in the contest when up against the pull of family. Without a word she got into the car and closed the door. Without a word, or a look, Sterne Parnell drove on.

CHAPTER SIX

EDEN'S first thought when she opened her eyes in Begonia Cottage on Tuesday was to hope that today might see Thomas come out of his coma. So far he had shown not the smallest sign that he was in any hurry to join the rest of the world.

Tired in mind as well as in body, Eden stayed in bed for a few minutes longer. Not that she was expecting Sterne to bring her up a cup of tea the way he had on Sunday—pigs would fly sooner—but she needed all her strength to see her through the day.

Reminded of Sunday, though, her thoughts drifted back to that dreadful day. In grim silence she and Sterne had entered the hospital, he to go and see Camilla, and she to hasten to Thomas.

There was no saying when Thomas would come out of his coma, but it was thought that things might be speeded up if she sat and talked to him of anything that might stir his consciousness.

She had been hoarse through talking when she had left his bedside that day, but nothing of what she said had brought forth any response. Fortunately she had not been required to do any talking when she had met Sterne again. He had nothing in particular he wanted to say to her, apparently, and since he was the last person with whom she wanted to strike up a conversation, she was able to save her voice.

On Monday morning she had gone down to the kitchen as soon as she was washed and dressed. The teapot had been warm and she realised that he must have made himself a cup of tea some time ago. She made herself a pot of tea and mused that this morning might see him returning to London to attend to his business interests.

She was in the middle of rinsing her cup and saucer when she heard him come into the kitchen. 'Ready?' he asked, and she realised that if he was going back to London he was prepared to take her to the hospital first.

She put down the tea cloth, and looked up to find his steady grey eyes on her. 'Thank you,' she murmured.

So began the start of a truce between them. Sterne had taken her to the hospital and had been there to take her back to Begonia Cottage later in the day. Eden guessed that he had probably been on the phone to his London office, but had decided that Camilla must come first.

'How's Camilla?' she asked him on the way home.

'A gash on her right leg is causing a few complications,' Sterne replied evenly. 'Otherwise, there's a slight improvement.'

'I'm glad—about the improvement,' Eden told him stiltedly, but since he could not bring himself to ask after Thomas, she felt she had nothing more she wanted to say.

That had been yesterday. Eden left her bed and took a bath wondering, half in fear and half in hope, what today would bring. Going down the stairs and into the kitchen, she halted when she saw that Sterne had unearthed a tea cosy from somewhere, and had placed it over the teapot to keep the tea hot for her.

Weak tears pricked her eyes at the kindly act. She poured herself a cup of tea and started to awake to the fact that her emotions must have been through quite an assault course these last few days if the mere fact of Sterne being kind to her could make her feel weepy.

Dry-eyed, she drank her tea. But she admitted that she must have softened to him somewhat when, car keys in hand, he joined her and asked the same question he had asked yesterday. This time, though, he added her name, and when he said, 'Ready, Eden?' she could just not find it within herself to be cross with him for all he was, and for all that he had done.

'I'll just get my coat,' she said, and slipped past him to run lightly up the stairs.

She spent most of the morning talking to an unresponsive Thomas. The only times that she left him were when the nursing staff came to attend to him. On these occasions she would wander outside his room to wait in the corridor, where she would try hard not to become disheartened that nothing she said was effective in reaching him.

It was a little after midday when she again returned to keep watch over Thomas. She resumed her seat by his bed and delved deeper into her memory for some shared activity of the past.

Ten minutes later she had disturbed what were painful memories for her. 'Do you remember when Mum had to go into hospital, and how awful it was without her?' Eden was so deep in remembering how like a rudderless ship they had been without Ruth that she did not hear the door behind her open. Nor was she aware that a tall, dark-haired man had entered and was standing watching her. Remembering the awful void that week without Ruth had made Eden's voice take on an urgent note, as she pleaded, 'Wake up, Thomas. Oh please, please wake up! You're my only family now and . . . and I don't want to be alone. If you won't wake up for your own sake—then *please*,' she implored him, 'please wake up for mine!'

She ended on a note of anguish, and a dry sob shook her. Suddenly, though, a sound in the room made her aware that she was not alone. As the sound of movement penetrated, Eden looked up, and the next moment Sterne Parnell had stepped into her line of vision.

Startled to see him there, her lovely blue eyes shining with emotion, Eden stared at him. 'They told me to talk to him,' she explained, her voice husky. 'But he won't wake up,' she choked. 'No matter what I say—I can't get through. He just won't wake up!'

'From the look of you, you'll crack before he wakes,' Sterne observed quietly, and as the door opened and a couple of nurses bustled in and Eden made for the door, she discovered to her surprise that Sterne was taking charge—and that she was letting him!

'Where are we going?' she asked when he clamped a hand beneath her elbow and guided her from the hospital and to his car.

'You're in need of some air,' he replied.

'But—Thomas!' she protested feebly.

'He'll still be here when you get back,' Sterne soothed, and assisted her into the Jaguar. He started the engine and moved off, and a short while later he pulled off the road. Eden had no objection to make when, indicating the hilly area around, he suggested, 'Come and stretch your legs.'

In silence she walked with him, and in silence she began to ascend with him the nearest and smallest of the hills. It was a remarkably sunny day for October, and as they reached the top of the hill and took in the fabulous scene spread out below, Eden began to recover some of her emotional equilibrium.

It was warm for the time of year, too, and when they came across a painted wooden seat and Sterne suggested that they took their ease, she had no demur to make.

For some time she looked at the restful view, and some sort of peace seemed to come over her. Minutes ticked by as she took in how the sunlight filtered through a clump of trees nearby, and how the leaves were changing colour.

Neither she nor Sterne said a word and, when all the odds were against it, Eden discovered that not only did she feel strangely tranquil within herself, but she felt tranquil with Sterne too! She even felt an empathy with him, and she could not but wonder why. She looked at him, but she was not quick enough to look away. For, as if sensing that her eyes were on him, he turned his head, and—smiled.

Her heart started to beat out the most wild of rhythms to see his smile, but before she turned her head the other way, she smiled back at him. *Am* I cracking up? she wondered. Because suddenly, when she knew that she hated him, she had the feeling that she liked him! And, when she knew that he had no time for her, she felt that *he* liked *her*!

She tried hard to concentrate on the view again, but all at once it began to impinge on her that—given all the trauma that surrounded her—sitting here with Sterne the way she was, she could almost imagine that she was happy!

Before she could delve any further into the depths of self-analysis, Eden quickly broke the silence. 'This is a beautiful place,' she commented.

'It is,' Sterne agreed, and as she turned to glance at him, he held her glance with his, and declared, 'Life—is full of surprises.' His eyes continued to hold hers, and suddenly Eden saw something in his eyes that set her heart racing.

'You—didn't know that there was th-this view—on the other side of the hill?' she asked—somewhat jerkily, she had to admit, because she could have sworn that she had seen admiration in his eyes, and even a glimmer of—affection?

'It's the first time I've been here,' he confessed.

'It's a magical place,' said Eden unthinkingly, and although it was sincerely said, she suddenly felt most peculiarly shy with him. 'How's Camilla today?' she asked in the hope of not giving him time to think her an idiot for her remark.

'She's still under sedation, but she's off the critical list,' Sterne replied. 'There'll be no holding her once her injured leg starts to knit.'

'I'm—pleased,' Eden told him, and she was. But talk of Camilla had brought with it memories of the hospital. 'I'd better get back,' she said, but suddenly, as Sterne helped her to her feet, the whole world seemed to still. For as he stood blocking her way, and she looked at him in enquiry, she became conscious of nothing—but only of him.

She thought he was going to kiss her, and she knew that if he did, she would not stop him. A sudden gust of wind broke the spell. She put a hand up to her wind-ruffled hair at the same time that Sterne raised a hand to smooth it. Their fingers touched and the whole of her body felt alive and tingling. She had never felt so aware of a man. It alarmed her because she had always been the one in charge of her being, but that no longer seemed to be the case.

She turned from him, going the other way up the grassy hillock. She wanted to continue to be the one in charge of herself. She did not want Sterne to be the one in charge—at least, she didn't think she did.

Eden realised that the sooner she got away from this place the better. 'Food,' Sterne said, when she was thinking that she was the only one who had gone a little crazy back there.

'Food?' she repeated.

'It's about time we had a proper meal,' Sterne let her into his thoughts as they surmounted the hill and started to go down the other side. 'I suggest we leave the tin opener in its drawer tonight, and go out to dinner.'

Eden hesitated, but she found that she did not have to answer immediately when, reaching his car, Sterne helped her inside and went round to the other door. Given that they missed breakfast each day and got what they could at the hospital, to return to Begonia Cottage to forage if they felt hungry, she thought they hadn't done too badly in the food department. But his invitation to dinner was so unexpected that she had to wonder—*was* she being as crazy as she thought a moment ago? Had they shared an empathy back there? Had Sterne felt that empathy too—or was it totally her imagination?

'I...' she began as he got in behind the wheel, and she was about to accept his invitation when, startlingly, she realised that but a minute ago she had felt quite attracted to him! 'Actually,' she began again, 'I haven't much of an appetite just lately. I think I'll stay in and see what I can find among the tinned stuff I brought with me.'

Eden owned that in facing the fact that she had been attracted to Sterne—however briefly—she in consequence felt considerably mixed up. She was glad, though, that she had turned down his offer, because he did not press his invitation.

Quite clearly, she thought, as they reached the hospital, Sterne had decided to fill his frame with something more suited to his palate than what he had so far eaten. Quite clearly too, his inbred manners had stretched to him doing her the courtesy of asking her to join him—but he wasn't breaking his heart that she had refused.

She had drummed up quite a dislike of him again by the time he had found a car parking space. No man, she thought, nettled, had ever so insulted her before by extending a dinner invitation only because he felt *obliged* so to do. She had her hand on the door handle as soon as the car stopped and, niggled, she would have left him without a word, only, 'Just a minute,' he halted her.

She turned to favour him with a imperious glance. 'Yes?' she questioned haughtily.

If Sterne was in turn slightly baffled by her change of manner, it did not show. 'Anything you fancy, in particular?' he asked, to make her the more baffled of the two. Her aloof manner faded under her puzzlement, and as she looked at him she saw that there was a smile in his eyes. 'I refuse to eat out of a tin tonight. Shall I get steak or do you have a preference for something else?' he asked.

'You're going shopping!'

'What's the matter,' he teased, his glance on her widening blue eyes, 'do you think shopping's beyond the capabilities of a mere male?'

Warmth started to melt the particles of ice that had been forming in her for him. Sterne had no intention of dining alone! All along, he had meant them to be dinner companions.

'I warn you,' she thought she had better tell him, 'I'm not a very good cook.'

'Charcoal, so I'm led to believe, is very good for the digestion,' he murmured, and as Eden could not help but burst out laughing, his eyes strayed down to her happily curving mouth.

Eden was not laughing when later that afternoon she stood in the corridor while her stepbrother was attended to. There was still no change in Thomas, but it was not thoughts of him that filled her head, but thoughts of Sterne Parnell.

There was no merriment in her eyes or on her mouth as she thought of how, so subtly that she had barely been aware of it, her hostility to that man had vanished. She recalled how, in the kitchen that very morning, she had found it impossible to be cross with him.

Perhaps he had changed too? Or had he? she pondered. Up until today he had not asked after Thomas, but the very fact that he had come along to see him had to mean something—didn't it? She switched her thoughts to the place on the hill where Sterne had taken her. She had thought the place magical, she remembered. It was there that she had felt he liked her, and had thought she had seen a look of affection in his eyes.

Her heart suddenly started to race as it had done up on that hill, but common sense quickly nullified all flights of fancy. Her heartbeat steadied down when common sense insisted that Sterne did *not* like her, so it was laughable to imagine that he might have some affection for her.

Alarm suddenly speared her, though, when she remembered how she had owned to feeling a moment's attraction for him. Good grief, she could not be attracted to him! One way or another, he meant to do Thomas harm, so how *could* she be attracted to Sterne?

'You can go in now,' a nurse coming from Thomas's room broke through Eden's panicky train of thought.

It was late afternoon when Eden saw Sterne again, and by that time she was sure that she was not in the least attracted to him, nor did she give a hoot whether he liked her or whether he didn't.

He saw her coming and extracted his long length from his car to come and open the passenger door. She did not want to talk to him of Thomas, nor, for that matter, of Camilla.

'How did the shopping expedition go?' she enquired pleasantly. 'Were you able to find your way around the supermarket?'

'Is the piped music compulsory?' he asked, and although she laughed in sympathy, she was quite happy that his ears could obviously have done without the shopping accompaniment.

Begonia Cottage was soon reached, but any notion she had that Sterne had purchased only the makings for a meal for that night were soon knocked on the head.

'What on earth have you got there?' she exclaimed when he opened the boot to reveal two large cardboard boxes.

'Your deplorable habit of leaving the house without breakfast will have to stop,' he told her with mock severity, and since he went without breakfast too, Eden had to laugh. 'You can carry that in,' he told her, thrusting a packet of bacon at her which had slipped off one of the boxes. 'I'll see to this lot.'

They had found a spare key to Begonia Cottage, and Eden had claimed it. She used it now to open up, and she took the packet of bacon into the kitchen.

Beneath every action since she had heard of Thomas's accident, there had lain a frightened centre of concern about him. But as Sterne brought the groceries in and they began to put them away, Eden realised that in other circumstances, she could quite enjoy this togetherness.

That realisation itself was enough to make her contradictory. 'I'm going to have a bath,' she told him shortly once the two cartons were empty.

She saw his head jerk up at her tone, but she was unrepentant. That was until, quite mildly, he said, 'Go and do that, Eden. You must be quite stiff from sitting in the same position for most of the day.'

She didn't want him to be nice to her, she *didn't*. It undermined her, as was proven in the way the softer person she really was replied, 'I won't be long. Can you hang on for dinner?'

Sterne smiled, a gentle smile that did the funniest things to her insides. 'I'll do more than that,' he told her, 'I'll peel the potatoes.'

Eden left him and went upstairs to run her bath and to try to find some toughness in her to resist being defeated by him at his smallest gesture. Basically, she argued, Sterne Parnell was the same as he had always been. He was a man who knew how to put on the charm when he wanted something. But he already knew where Camilla was, so what—with his subtle brand of charm just now—did he want this time?

Eden felt better for her bath. Though when she began to feel that she wanted to look her best that night, she overcame the feeling. It was only dinner for two at home, for goodness' sake—and she was cooking it! She'd look ridiculous standing over a spitting grill wearing one of her stunning numbers!

She left her room wearing a pastel blue velvet jumpsuit. Sterne was still in the kitchen when she went in, and was uncorking a bottle of wine. He looked over to her, but she slid her glance from him. He had been busy, she saw, taking in the fact that the table was laid, and that there was a pan of peeled potatoes on the stove.

'I'll take over,' she volunteered.

'You've heard of cooking with wine,' he said, as, looking into her eyes, he handed her a glass.

'Thank you.' She accepted it from him, but in spite of herself, he had amused her, and she was not quick enough to hide her amused expression. His expression, though, as he stared at the evidence of good humour on her mouth, was all at once deadly serious.

Her own smile disappeared and for a few seconds she felt that the very air between them was suspended. So intently did Sterne seem to be studying her then that she wanted to ask him what the matter was.

But her throat was suddenly choked, and she could not ask—a moment later Eden wondered if she had imagined anything out of the ordinary at all. For although it was abruptly that Sterne turned from her, she had never heard his voice more casual than when, already on his way to the door, he commented, 'At the risk of being thought a male chauvinist, I'll leave you to do the slaving-over-a-hot-stove bit, while I go and freshen up.'

She started work on the meal and could not but think that when her imagination chose to go overboard, it certainly went overboard! There hadn't been so much as a second of anything suspended just then! She pushed Sterne out of her mind.

Half an hour later the dinner had come together, but Sterne was still upstairs. Eden strained the vegetables and put them in serving dishes in a warm oven. Still there was no sign of Sterne, nor, as she listened, was there any sound of him.

Feeling ridiculous she could nevertheless not deny a sensation of alarm. Quickly she went to the foot of the stairs. 'Sterne!' she shouted from the bottom.

She had one foot on the stairs ready to go up to see if he was all right when his answering, 'Yes?' floated down the stairs.

'If you don't come now, your starter will get cold,' she shouted back grumpily. She went back to the kitchen to decide that the worry and strain over Thomas had been too much. Since the starter was melon, and since it had come out of the fridge, she doubted that it would get any colder.

Eden had sipped only spasmodically at the glass of wine which Sterne had handed her, and she took what remained in her glass over to the table. Having made a fool of herself with regard to the cold starter, she decided that she was not going to wait for Sterne to come down only to have him tell her she should not have waited.

She had just picked up her knife, however, when he came in through the door she had left open. 'Sorry to be late,' he apologised, taking his place and eyeing the melon as if he considered her remark about it going cold a joke. 'I've been hunting high and low for a clean pair of socks.'

Somehow the idea of Sterne doing anything so mundane as hunt for a clean pair of socks amused her. Eden looked at him and could not straighten the definite upward curve to her mouth when she volunteered, 'If you'll leave your socks out, I'll swill them through if you like.'

'Your courage does you credit, madam,' Sterne replied without so much as a glimmer of a smile, 'but I'm quite capable of washing them myself.'

'If they're that bad,' Eden answered, knowing for sure that there was nothing wrong with his socks, or his feet either for that matter, 'then you're welcome.'

Suddenly, though, they were both laughing, and she was struck by how laughter suited him. He should laugh more, she thought, but she guessed that her own laughter over something so simple was because, strung up over Thomas, she had needed to laugh—or break down.

The thought all at once came to her that perhaps Sterne had known that. Had he known? Had he perhaps seen, without her noticing, how on a knife edge she felt inwardly? Had he seen and deliberately set out to make her laugh and forget her worries for a while?

The meal progressed without her being able to come to any conclusion. They were on the cheese and biscuits course when she felt his eyes on her and she looked across the table to him. He was indeed looking at her, she saw, but the light and easy manner he had shown throughout the meal was suddenly gone.

The word, 'What...?' seemed to be jerked from her, and she was not much further forward in finding out what his suddenly severe expression was all about when he questioned, 'Morrisey—he's your only family?'

Eden knew then that Sterne had heard her saying as much to Thomas when she had been imploring him to wake up. 'Yes,' she answered, but she started to be wary of Sterne again.

'And your—love—for him is purely that of a stepsister for a stepbrother?' he queried, his casual tone belied by the severity of his expression.

She knew that he was anything but casual, and she delayed answering while she tried to see what was behind his question. It did not take long. Everything that involved her and Sterne revolved around Thomas and Camilla, so Eden realised that what lay behind Sterne's question was his conviction that Thomas did not in truth love Camilla.

'If you're thinking that Thomas's love for me might be that of more than a brother, forget it,' she told him shortly. 'Thomas is in love with Camilla and...'

'That,' Sterne cut in, his casual tone abruptly gone, 'was not what I asked.'

Eden knew that that was not the way he had phrased his question, and there was a lot else she could have told him besides the truth that Thomas was in love with his ward. But she was afraid to give him ammunition which might come firing back at her or Thomas at a later date—although for the life of her she could not see how, so she pretended she had taken his question at face value.

'My love for Thomas,' she told Sterne coldly, 'is the love of the sister which, even though we don't share the same blood, I truly feel I am.'

She had ended with a hostile glare at Sterne but, to her surprise, his harsh expression had gone, and it was most pleasantly and with a deal of charm that he murmured, 'Now why couldn't you have said that in the first place?'

Eden threw him a withering look, but somehow she felt out of her depth. She stood up. 'Goodnight,' she said shortly, and abruptly left him.

She was not sure who she felt most angry with when upstairs she decided that she might as well go to bed. She took her night things into the bathroom and washed and changed, and wondered about Sterne. His charm when he chose to exert it was colossal, there was no getting away from that. But need she have... run away—as if overpowered by it?

Two minutes later Eden was rejecting the idea that she had in any way been overpowered by Sterne Parnell's charm. She left the bathroom and went to her room and climbed into bed. More time elapsed when she was certain that she was immune to any charm he might happen to have. All that had been wrong with her when she had felt unable to stay in the same room with him had been anger.

Another ten minutes went by, and Eden knew just why she had been so angry. Sterne had been asking her about her love for Thomas. That had brought thoughts of Thomas to her mind. Thoughts of Thomas and Camilla.

She had every justification for being angry, Eden concluded. Thomas was a gentle and a kind man and he had been terribly hurt when Sterne had told him why he was so dead set against him marrying his ward. Of course Sterne did not know that as soon as Thomas was acquainted with the details of his father's past, he had said he could no longer marry Camilla, but... Eden sighed and, switching off her light, snuggled down the bed to try to sleep. But sleep was far away.

Wide awake, she hoped and prayed, first, that Thomas would get well. She was in the middle of hoping that, secondly, Camilla had been able to talk him out of his decision and that they would marry, when a sound in the next room told her that Sterne was no longer downstairs.

She supposed the thickness of the walls in the cottage had deadened the sound of him coming up the stairs. She sent hate vibes through the partitioning wall and turned her back on it. Then, as an aid to falling asleep, she tried to think of nothing.

The trouble was that her head seemed to be filled either with Thomas, or Camilla, but mostly with Sterne Parnell.

A couple of wide-awake hours had passed when Eden discovered that her thoughts on Sterne had mellowed somewhat. It was still without question that he had more than his fair share of charm but, she found herself thinking, was it natural charm, or was it put on? Was he after something, or in fact—nothing?

Eden turned over in bed and again tried to go to sleep, but she was too restless, too fidgety, too mixed up, and she wondered why the dickens that was so—what was wrong with her?

When she started to feel guilty that, against all the odds, Sterne had been to see Thomas, but she had not been to see Camilla, Eden threw back the covers and got out of bed. She'd had enough of thoughts which she could not find an answer to, without guilt arriving to complicate matters.

Vaguely Eden was aware of some unthought but sound intention of getting up extra early in the morning to tackle the evening's washing up. But since it didn't look as though she was going to do anything for the next couple of hours but lie awake, she decided that there was no time like the present.

Convinced that Sterne had not so much as cleared the table after their meal, she donned her robe and slipped noiselessly from her room. Noiselessly too, she entered the kitchen-cum-dining-room, switched on the lights—and stopped dead. It was as neat as a new pin!

More guilt entered her soul that she had, without a second's thought, left Sterne all the clearing up to do. She took a few steps into the room and was chastened that there was not a thing in the kitchen to keep her occupied. She turned, intending to go back to bed, but suddenly her heart set up a tumultuous beating. For unheard by her, Sterne had come to stand in the doorway. Speechlessly she stared at him, her eyes taking in that he was bare-footed, trouser-clad, and bare-chested.

'I d-didn't mean to disturb you,' she apologised huskily, and realised that she herself felt more than a little disturbed.

'Anything wrong?' he enquired quietly, his eyes intent on hers.

'I couldn't sleep,' she explained, and she took a step forwards to indicate that she intended going back to bed.

'You've been worrying about your stepbrother?' Sterne enquired, stepping to one side, but going with her as she went back up the stairs.

Eden nodded. 'Goodnight,' she said for the second time that night.

'That's becoming a habit,' Sterne teased, as though to send her to bed on a light note.

Eden smiled as she remembered that the first night they had stayed in Begonia Cottage she had twice wished him goodnight. 'I'm sorry I left you with all the clearing away and the washing up,' she paused to apologise, and found she was smiling more broadly when Sterne caught on and exclaimed,

'My sainted aunt, you didn't go down at this time of the night to clear up the kitchen!'

'Stick around—you could learn a lot,' she laughed. But suddenly, Sterne's eyes on her laughing face became serious, and every instinct in Eden was urging her on her way.

Intending to obey that instinct, she was nearer to Sterne's door than he was, and as she went to move out of the way, so, almost as if he too was obeying similar instincts, he moved to enter his room. Somehow they collided.

And having collided, they touched. She put out a hand to steady herself and her hand met his bare chest. A tingling started inside her and when she knew that she should withdraw her hand, she seemed powerless to do so. She heard Sterne groan, and as though he was tingling too, one of his arms came about her. She looked up, and his head came down to meet hers.

Never had she known an experience like that kiss. It seemed to charge every fibre of her being. As Sterne wrapped both his arms about her and held her close to him, Eden wrapped her arms around him and clung on.

'My dear...' he breathed as his kiss broke, and, thrilled by his endearment, her lips parted in silent plea for him to kiss her again.

She moaned faintly when his mouth again lingered on her parted lips, and her hands clutched at his naked back.

Minutes, endless uncounted minutes ticked by as Sterne kissed her eyes and trailed kisses to her ears and down the arched column of her throat.

When he pushed the material of her robe and nightdress to one side with one hand, she pressed herself to him, and delighted in his touch when his mouth sought the softness of her breast.

'Oh, Sterne!' she cried, wanting to get closer, yet closer to him still.

She knew she was going to get that wish when, as if he had read her mind, he gently lifted her up in his arms, and carried her to her bedroom.

As gently, he laid her down on her bed, and eased the ache she had for him to be near by lying down with her on the double mattress.

Long and deeply he kissed her, and Eden was enchanted by his tenderness and the caress of his hands at her back. She clutched on to him hard when, holding her close against him with one arm, his other hand moved to the front of her and he gently captured one of her breasts in a whisper of a touch.

Unhurriedly he removed her robe, and kissed her as he tenderly slid the thin straps of her nightdress from her shoulders.

'You're so beautiful,' he murmured, his voice thick in his throat, and Eden felt the exquisite torment of his mouth as his lips saluted each naked pink-tipped breast in turn.

'Oh, Sterne!' she could not help crying out again, and she felt such a fire in her that she had no thought for anything but him.

That was until, as if her inexperienced ardour was enchanting to him, Sterne alarmed her by making her realise that they had gone too far for her to back out. Not that she had any thought of backing out when, with a still gentle touch, he started to remove her last remnant of covering completely.

It was then that nerves caught at Eden, and made her want to grab her nightdress back. Real panic hit her when she saw one of his hands go to the waistband of his trousers. And somehow, when he kissed her again, she found that she was just not as mindless to everything as she had been a few moments ago.

When he pulled back from her and told her, oh so softly, 'I'll try not to hurt you, my dear,' she started to shake, and she knew she could not go through with it.

'I...' she gasped and, pushing him from her, she scrambled from the bed and grabbed for her robe. Further words failed her, but as she looked at Sterne and saw that he seemed as speechless as she, she just had to force the words out, 'You've hurt me enough. Through Thomas—you've hurt me.'

She saw Sterne's expression harden, and when he too left the bed, she backed away. 'This has got nothing to do with Morrisey,' he grated. 'It's between you and me!'

'Dear me, Sterne,' mocked Eden, wanting him from her room with all speed, but nowhere near certain if she was going about it the right way. 'Don't tell me you've forgotten your opinion that I'm as big a con-artist as my stepbrother!'

He cast her an exasperated look. 'Don't be stupid...' he began, but Eden had broken out into a cold sweat at what had so nearly happened, and she was not receptive to anything he said.

'I may have been stupid enough to have let you catch me at a weak moment,' she cut in icily. 'But if I hadn't come to my senses when I did—if I'd allowed you to let me forget what you've done to my stepbrother...' she broke off to gulp for breath '...then come morning, I should be hating not only you—but myself!'

For the briefest moment she thought Sterne had paled. For less than a second, she thought she had seen hurt in his eyes at what she had just said. But it was brought home to her just how mixed up she must be to have imagined anything of the sort. For there was nothing wrong with his colour, and there was not a sign of hurt about him, when, just before he turned and strolled carelessly through the door, he mockingly let fall, 'My God—all this for a trifling physical interlude!'

CHAPTER SEVEN

EDEN was still smarting from Sterne's parting remark when, as daylight broke, she opened the door to the kitchen-cum-dining-room. She was still hating him for the fact that he had dared to degrade those moments of her teetering on the brink of giving herself to him as a 'trifling physical interlude'.

Passing underneath what was his bedroom, she glared at the ceiling and went to put the kettle to boil. The kettle felt warm and her glance went to the teapot. She had thought that Sterne was still in bed, but the tea cosy which he had placed over the teapot made her realise that although he had probably returned to his room, he was up and about.

Eden was scornful that, despite the way they had parted, he had found sufficient civility this morning to put a cosy on the teapot for her. She carried through with her intention and, filling the kettle, set it to boil, and emptied the contents of the teapot away. She wanted him doing *nothing* for her!

Her tea made, she poured herself a cup and took it over to the dining-table. She remembered the bacon in the fridge—it could stay there!

Not hungry, she glanced around the room and was overcome by such a restlessness of spirit that she found it difficult to sit still. Damn you, Sterne Parnell! she thought angrily, but she knew exactly why she damned him. It was he who had triggered off this restlessness in her. Up until last night she had always been in charge of her own person. Last night—he had very nearly changed all that. Last night, he had kissed her, and it had not stopped there. She had been kissed before, but it had been *his* kiss which made made her forget standards which, until then, had seemed inbuilt in her. Previously she had not had to think about it, she had just known that it was not right. So—what was so right about Sterne Parnell that she had wanted him to be the one; that she had wanted him to be her lover?

Unable to sit still any longer, she took her cup and saucer over to the sink. This morning she knew that last night her senses had played her false, but she was never more glad that she had come to them in time.

The feeling of restlessness within her grew stronger and she wished with all her being that the parents were alive, and that Thomas was well, and that things were just as they used to be. The stark reality of it was, though, that things were not as they used to be, nor could they be.

Feeling like some nomad, with no settled home, she just then heard the outside door open. She had thought Sterne was upstairs, but evidently he had been out.

She had not paused to give thought to how she would feel the next time that they met. But suddenly there flashed in front of her a picture of herself, as near naked as made no difference, with Sterne, his chest bare, looking down at her as they lay on her bed.

Scarlet colour stormed her cheeks, and as the kitchen door opened she swung abruptly round to stare unseeing out of the kitchen window.

'I've just rung the hospital,' Sterne addressed her back in level tones.

Her high colour subsided under her sudden panic for her stepbrother. 'Thomas?' she questioned, and swung round to face Sterne, who did not keep her in suspense, but told her,

'There's no change in Morrisey.'

Relief that Thomas was no worse gave Eden space to remember her bitter regrets about the way she had been with Sterne last night.

'I suppose I must thank you for deigning to enquire after my stepbrother,' she said aloofly, and not a little ungraciously, she had to admit as she caught a glint of ice in Sterne's eyes.

'In answer to your non-enquiry about my ward,' he went on shortly, 'Camilla has made remarkable progress since yesterday.'

'I'm—glad,' Eden told him stiltedly.

'So am I,' he replied coolly, and added crisply, 'As soon as she can stand the journey, she'll be transferred to a London hospital.'

'You're having her transf...!'

'Of course!' he cut in bluntly, and to Eden's chagrin, just as though he thought she was some kind of idiot, he explained, 'My work is in London. Once Camilla's settled there, I can do my job, and visit her daily.'

'It seems an ideal arrangement.' Eden borrowed some of his cool manner to reply. And, because she couldn't resist it, she added, 'It's a wonder to me that you've been able to leave your work at all!'

'Most men can manage two days in an emergency,' he clipped, and as she grappled with a most peculiar sense of being cut adrift to hear, from the sound of it, that Sterne was going back to London today, he confirmed that that was exactly what he was going to do. 'I've a meeting in London at midday. If you're ready, I'll give you a lift to the hospital.'

Only a short while ago she had decided that she wanted him doing nothing for her. Suddenly, though, as realisation started to set in that when Sterne went back to London, she might never see him again, she discovered that she did not know her own mind for two minutes together. For she could not see any reason why, in this last instance, she should not accept a lift as far as the hospital.

'Ready when you are,' she said coolly.

When Sterne stopped the car at the hospital Eden was unsure if it was his intention to visit Camilla before he made for London. She flicked him a glance of enquiry, but it was met with such a look of cold impatience that Eden could not help realising that Sterne could not wait for her to vacate his car so that he could be on his way.

She quickly changed her look of enquiry to one of aloof dislike, and left the car as though the devils of hell were at her heels. She was nearly at the hospital entrance when Sterne caught up with her to show that he was not impatient to be away, but more impatient with her. She ignored him. When he went one way to where Camilla was, Eden, without a word, went the other.

That Wednesday morning dragged by with interminable slowness, and she had never felt more despondent. There was still no change in Thomas's condition when she left him at lunch time to walk around to try to lift her depressed spirits. She endeavoured not to think about Sterne Parnell, but as she remembered that he had a meeting at midday, she found she was wondering if his meeting was over, or if he was having a working lunch.

Abruptly she dismissed him from her mind. Huh! As if she cared if he never ate again! Mystifyingly, when she had set her mind to not think about him, she could not escape the memory of him, gentle, tender even, as he had taken her on a voyage of discovery about herself last night. He... Rapidly, Eden wiped him from her mind. Swiftly she turned about and, as if to outpace her thoughts, she hurried back to the hospital.

She was again out in the corridor at half past two when she experienced a return of the guilt which had visited her last night because she had not been to see Camilla. Conscience had another stab when Eden realised that now that Sterne had gone back to London, his ward would be without visitors at all.

On that thought, she started on the route which Sterne took on his visits to Camilla. Making an enquiry of the Sister-in-Charge, she was told that it might cheer Miss Rodgers up to have a visitor.

Camilla had a room to herself, was surrounded by flowers, was nursing a black eye, and was looking very sorry for herself until she recognised her visitor.

'Eden!' Her face lit up as Eden approached her bed. 'Oh, I'm so glad to see you!' she declared. 'I've been wanting you to come, but I thought Thomas needed you more than I did. How is he?' she asked, her bright smile fading. 'Has he...'

'There's no change in his condition,' Eden told her carefully, wondering just how much or how little Camilla had been told.

'He's still in a coma?' Camilla asked worriedly, revealing that little had been kept back from her.

'I'm afraid so,' answered Eden gently, and realised that Camilla had built up a fine head of frustrated feeling when she exploded,

'God, I wish they'd let me see him!'

'You're not fit enough to leave your bed yet,' Eden soothed.

'So *they* say!' cried Camilla, but forgot about *them*, to ask quietly, 'How does he look? Is he cut? Is he...'

'Of the two of you,' Eden told her, 'you look the more bruised.'

'Thank goodness for that!' breathed Camilla, going on, 'They've told me that his internal injuries are on the mend, but...' The next five minutes were taken up with a question-and-answer session about Thomas—Camilla asking the questions, and Eden supplying the answers. 'Oh, I do hope he's going to be all right!' Camilla cried when she had, for the moment, run out of questions. 'I can't bear it that...' Her voice broke and all Eden could do was to try to think up something to take her mind off her distress. Poor Camilla; unable to see Thomas, she must have been going demented ever since the news of his condition had been broken to her.

'Apart from wanting to see him, of course, is there anything you need?' she asked. 'Anything I can bring you?'

Camilla shook her head. 'No thanks, Eden,' she said, finding a smile, but as her smile fell away, she added, 'My guardian, via the phone, via his secretary, has ensured that I have everything I need.'

From her tone, Eden gathered that Camilla's guardian was not her most favourite person just then. 'That's—kind of him,' she replied in her best placatory manner.

'Kind!' Camilla exclaimed. 'After what he's done! If he hadn't been so determined to split Thomas and me up, none of this would have happened!'

Eden had had much the same thoughts herself and, if memory served, she had not hung back from telling Sterne so. But, most oddly then, when all her thoughts and feelings were on the side of Thomas and the girl he loved, she found that she was defending Sterne!

'He *is* your guardian,' she murmured, but only to have Camilla declare warmly,

'In my view, he takes his duties as my guardian much too seriously.'

'That's natural enough, surely,' this other person in Eden who seemed determined to defend Sterne offered up.

Camilla was in no way mollified, and on account of what had happened to Thomas she refused to be appeased when Eden mentioned that he had been so worried about her that he had not been to work for two days.

'He deserves to be worried,' she sniffed. 'But he's gone back to London now, and I hope he stays there. Poor you,' she sympathised, 'with the cottage so conveniently near, it must have been awful to have to stay there with him.'

'Awful?' Eden questioned, and for the life of her she could not at that moment remember when it had been so very awful.

'Of course, awful,' Camilla replied. 'How could it be otherwise? With Thomas lying so very ill, you must be hating Sterne as much as I'm hating him just now.'

Eden went from her visit with Camilla back to sit with Thomas. She had no clear recollection of quite what she had said to Camilla in answer to her assumption that she hated Sterne, but the words of agreement that she hated him, staggeringly, refused to leave her throat!

Sitting beside Thomas, she just had to take a moment out from talking to him, for her own private thoughts. Because suddenly she discovered that she no longer held Sterne responsible for everything that had happened!

Astounded by the way her thoughts were going, Eden suddenly realised that she had been most unfair to blame him for Thomas's accident. From the sound of it, the brakes on Charlie Oakes's car could have failed at any time—they would have gone anyway, whether Thomas had been driving around in the Lake District or wherever he had been!

Trying to come to terms with this new line of thinking, she was further startled when she found that she was stopping to see things from Sterne's point of view. Wasn't it only natural that Sterne, in receipt of the information that the private detectives had given him, should go all out to protect his ward?

Not that it made it any better that he had called in a firm of private investigators in the first place, but... Abruptly, Eden's thoughts came to a stunned halt. For suddenly, and to take her breath away, she just knew that she was in love with Sterne Parnell!

Stupefied, Eden was in a no man's land of confusion as she tried to eject that startling fact from her mind. Try as she might, though, the fact that she loved Sterne Parnell, and had done almost from the start, refused to be ejected—just as it refused to be denied.

Only then did she begin to understand why, when from the very first they had been antagonists, he had had the power to make her laugh. Only then did she realise why his kiss last night had been so right, and why she had wanted him to be her lover. She was in love with him, and love, real love, had made a nonsense of her high-flown touch-me-not standards.

For a while she was not sure if she was glad or sorry that their lovemaking had come to nought. But as she recalled how nerves, shyness, call it what you will, had started to get to her, she could only be glad that she had not made that final commitment. Because, in remembering, she was reminded of the hurt Thomas had received at Sterne's hands.

Eden looked at her stepbrother's face, 'Oh, Thomas,' she cried aloud. Thomas, dear, sensitive Thomas, had been in blissful ignorance of his father's past until Sterne had uncovered the truth.

She remembered how, last night, Sterne had ground out, 'This has got nothing to do with Morrisey. It's between you and me!' But as her gaze stayed with her stepbrother, Eden knew that there could be nothing between her and Sterne while Thomas was the way he was.

A very short while later, she was blaming the fact that she and Sterne had been so as one last night for the thought that he might want anything more from her than a—trifling physical interlude.

It was early evening when she left Thomas's bedside. But by then she had accepted stoically that Sterne was not more than passingly interested in her—and only physically at that. Indeed, he had not hesitated to tell her so. And if she wanted more proof she had only to remember the way he had been with her that morning.

Eden stepped from the hospital feeling she could be fairly positive that, rather than love her a little, Sterne Parnell hated her a lot.

Suddenly Eden stood stock-still. Many were the times since Sunday when she had stood in the hospital forecourt and felt close to tears. But this time, as she fought against the need to weep, her held-back tears were not on account of her stepbrother. They were on account of Sterne, and his kindness.

For while there were cars parked which she did not recognise, there amongst the vehicles was one car which she did recognise—it was her own car.

Hate her as she had faced that he must, Sterne had all the same given a thought to the fact that, without him and his car, she was stuck for transport. How it had been achieved was irrelevant; the fact was that Sterne must have arranged for her car to be delivered.

Eden ate a solitary dinner that night, and went to her solitary bed. She slept only fitfully, and got up the next morning to drink a solitary cup of tea and to accept that she was missing Sterne. In the short time she had known him, he had become part of her life.

She was about to get ready to go to the hospital when suddenly the front doorbell rang. Ridiculously, her first thought was that it was Sterne, and her heart was beating energetically as she went to answer the door.

Eden forced a smile when she recognised Mrs Fox, the next-door owner of Begonia Cottage. Her smile swiftly faded though when Mrs Fox began, 'The hospital have just rung and...' She broke off when she saw how Eden had lost some of her colour. 'Oh, there's nothing to worry about. Your stepbrother's doing well!' she exclaimed quickly, and went on to tell how Miss Rodgers had persuaded the Sister-in-Charge to ring as soon as she could to break the good news that Mr Morrisey had come out of his coma.

'He's come out...!' Eden gasped.

'He came out of it this morning,' Mrs Fox beamed. 'I rather think Miss Rodgers may have had something to do with it,' she added, 'because she was with him when it happened.'

Oh, bless you, Camilla, Eden thought, and could not wait to get to the hospital to see Thomas for herself.

She had to wait to see him, however, for when she arrived at the hospital, she found that Thomas was to undergo a series of tests that morning.

'Mr Morrisey is no longer on the critical list,' the Sister told her pleasantly, if pointedly.

From that Eden gathered that the freedom she'd had to visit Thomas at any time had just been curtailed. But she was too happy for him to be in any way offended.

'If you get the chance, will you tell him that I'll be in to see him this afternoon?' she smiled.

'Certainly,' the Sister answered, and bustled away to her duties.

It crossed Eden's mind to go and see Camilla, but she felt in too emotional a state just then. Eden realised that she needed to get herself more together before she thanked Camilla for doing for Thomas what her own voice had not been able to do.

Leaving the hospital, she went to buy some fruit for Thomas and some flowers to brighten up his room, and to purchase a pretty bed jacket for Camilla. But, her shopping done, she still had hours to fill before she should return to the hospital. Taking the things she had bought back to her car, Eden started her car up and drove along with no clear idea of where she was going.

When she recognised that she was in the same beautiful area where Sterne had brought her on Tuesday, she stopped the car, realising that, even if she had not been aware of where she was going, her subconscious must have known.

Drawn to walk up the small hillside, Eden ambled down the other side and took her ease on the bench where she had sat with Sterne.

She stayed feasting her eyes on the magnificent view for some time, and trying to recapture some of the peace and tranquillity she had felt before, but the peace she sought evaded her. She went back to her car and was aware that to recognise that she was in love with Sterne had brought her no joy.

On the off-chance that Thomas's tests were over, she drove back to the hospital. He was asleep when she was allowed to see him, but it was a natural, healing sleep. Eden stayed only a minute and tiptoed out, to go along to see if it was convenient to visit Camilla.

'Isn't it great!' Camilla exclaimed ecstatically the moment she saw her.

'It's wonderful!' Eden said from the heart. 'And we've you to thank that Thomas...'

'It was nothing,' grinned Camilla, overjoyed that Thomas had found the start of the road to recovery.

'What happened?' asked Eden. 'I mean, how...'

'Oh, it was marvellous!' Camilla declared, and in revealing how Thomas had come out of his coma, she incidentally revealed also how very much in love with him she was. 'As you know,' she began, 'they said that I wasn't fit enough to go and see him.'

'They changed their minds?' Eden prompted.

'No,' Camilla denied. 'Well, not until one of the nursing staff found me half-way down the corridor. As Staff Nurse Corrigan said, when with the speed of light she found a wheelchair, "I may as well push you the rest of the way as push you back to bed."'

'You were on your way to see Thomas—without permission!'

'Wouldn't you be?' Camilla replied. 'I've lain in this bed getting in more and more of a stew ever since they told me about Thomas. Last night, or rather, about six o'clock this morning, I couldn't take it any more.'

Eden had only met Camilla a couple of times, but suddenly she was liking her more and more. 'You've suffered no ill effects?' she asked in some concern.

Camilla shook her head. 'Seeing Thomas has been the best medicine in the world for me. The doctor visited me a short while ago and he said that—if I behaved myself—I could go along and see Thomas again this afternoon. Have you seen Thomas?' she thought to ask.

'He was asleep when I peeped in just now,' Eden told her, and decided on the spur of the moment that since Camilla would probably want Thomas all to herself, 'I thought I'd look back early this evening. Did he come out of his coma as soon as he heard your voice?' she asked.

Again Camilla shook her head. 'For the first ten minutes I could have been talking to a brick wall for all the response I got,' she said. 'But the longer it went on, the more frequent were the assessing looks Staff Nurse Corrigan gave me, and I just knew that any minute now she was going to turn the wheelchair about and push me out of there. I suppose that in the end it was a sense of uselessness, frustration and anxiety all mixed together which culminated in my being so beside myself that suddenly I found myself shouting "If you don't wake up this minute, Thomas Morrisey, I'll never forgive you!" I was so ashamed afterwards,' Camilla confessed, 'but before I could grovel and ask Thomas to forgive me—just like that—he opened his eyes.'

When Eden reached Begonia Cottage after her visit, she made herself something to eat, and thought that a spot of vacuuming and dusting would not come amiss.

By six o'clock the downstairs was looking considerably brighter for the attention it had been given. The upstairs had been attended to as well, although Eden had felt weak at the knees as she'd decided to enter the room which Sterne had used. By half past six she was bathed, changed, and was grabbing a quick cup of tea before she went to the hospital.

The alteration in Thomas when she saw him was little short of dramatic. The various tubes he had been attached to were removed and he was propped up on pillows, washed and shaven, and looking much more like her dear stepbrother.

'Oh, love,' she exclaimed, and almost wept. 'Can I ask how you're feeling?'

'Fragile,' he smiled, 'and guilty.'

Fragile, Eden could understand. 'Guilty?' she questioned.

'Guilty in the extreme,' he told her. 'The brakes on Charlie Oakes's car started to play up around the time that I met Camilla. I knew darned well that I should have got them fixed only, somehow, I never seemed to have the time.' He looked appalled by his negligence when he exclaimed, 'I could have killed Camilla!'

'Well, you didn't,' Eden told him briskly, and quickly changed the subject. 'Did they tell you that Camilla disobeyed orders to come and see you this morning?'

Thomas smiled. 'She's great, isn't she?'

'She is,' Eden agreed wholeheartedly.

'I saw her this afternoon,' Thomas went on. 'She tells me you're staying at Begonia Cottage.'

'You don't mind, do you?'

'Of course I don't, daft,' he scolded, but he frowned when as if trying to remember, he confessed, 'I'm a bit confused still, but how did you hear about the accident? Were you on your way to Begonia Cottage or were you still in London? You said you were going to start out straight away that Friday, but...'

'I did start out straight away,' Eden told him. 'Well, more or less. Only I—er—had company.'

'You were bringing someone with you?'

'Not exactly—bringing,' she replied, and not wishing to overtire him, she wanted to leave it there.

'Go on,' Thomas prodded. 'I've a feeling I shan't sleep a wink if you don't tell me all of it.'

'Well...' Eden began, feeling uncomfortable as she confessed, 'I know I'm an idiot, but when you phoned, I rang Camilla's guardian to tell him that I'd heard from you.'

'You rang him!' Thomas's expression was a picture of disbelief.

'I said I was an idiot,' she murmured weakly, 'but I fully expected to be on my way to you and Camilla within five minutes of putting down the phone from talking to him.'

'Something went wrong?'

She nodded. 'When I went out to my car I'd got a puncture. Sterne Parnell had arrived before I could get the wheel off. He changed the wheel and then tailed me.' She noticed that Thomas had fallen silent, and she hurried up to get the rest of it said. 'No matter how I tried, I just couldn't shake him and—well, to cut it short, when I got as near to Begonia Cottage as I dared, I checked into a hotel. Sterne—Parnell,' she quickly added his surname, 'did the same. When he rang his housekeeper, she told him that the police had been in touch. He rang the police, and...'

'And then came and told you?' Thomas finished for her, and when she again nodded, he was typically thinking of others first, when he said, 'Poor Eden, it must have been a dreadful shock.'

'It was,' she agreed, and found that she just had to tell him, 'Sterne—Parnell was very kind. When he saw how...'

'He was *kind*?' Thomas interrupted to query, and to incidentally remind her that Sterne's dealings with him had been anything but kindly.

Eden had never thought she might be pulled two ways by love. But suddenly her family love for her stepbrother was being opposed by the love she had for Sterne—Thomas's enemy. And, of the two, she discovered that the love she had for Sterne, that different kind of love, was much, much the stronger.

'I don't know what else you'd call it,' she felt she had to insist. 'When he saw how his news had knocked me for six, he was most—er—understanding, and...'

'Understanding?' Thomas interrupted her again. But, unexpectedly, he was grinning as, quite unexpectedly too, he commented, 'It's to be hoped his understanding holds up when he learns that his latest plan to split Camilla and me up has gone down the plughole.'

Eden felt all chewed up inside, and she was disturbed that hostilities were still going on, but she was unable to do anything about it as she asked, 'What plan?'

'Sterne Parnell made plans for Camilla to be transferred to a London nursing home early this afternoon. Unfortunately, nobody thought to tell Camilla until the private ambulance arrived outside.'

'She—refused to go?' Eden suggested, feeling pale.

'She threatened to scream the hospital down if anyone tried to wheel her within ten yards of the ambulance,' Thomas said proudly.

'Oh, dear,' murmured Eden faintly, and Thomas smiled.

'I've discovered,' he said, 'that Camilla has quite a lot going for her in the "strong will" department.'

'But—can't Sterne Parnell, as her guardian, have her transferred whether she wants to go or not?' Eden queried.

'Not if her temperature starts to destabilise, as it did then,' he replied. 'No doctor worthy of the name would sanction her travelling all that way with a high temperature—especially when she's recovering quite well here.'

'I suppose not,' Eden said slowly, and she felt her throat go dry and her heart begin to flutter, when Thomas smiled.

'Camilla's guardian may have thought he'd seen the last of this hospital, but, since he's such a stickler for duty, it's my guess that he'll be up here again before this coming weekend is over.'

Eden had thought she might never see Sterne again. 'Do you think so?' she asked the still smiling Thomas when she had found her voice. And, if her life had depended on it, she could not hold down the smile that started somewhere in the very heart of her, and which appeared on her face sunnily to far outshine the smile that Thomas wore.

CHAPTER EIGHT

WHEN Eden awoke on Friday, her first action was to smile. Her look went dreamy: she might, she just might, see Sterne again this weekend.

She got out of bed knowing that she would not see him before tomorrow lunch time—if then. What with the Friday night traffic and everything, she didn't think he would make tracks for the hospital as soon as he left his office today. It could well be that he would arrive too late in the evening to see Camilla anyway. To Eden's mind, it seemed far more sensible that he would start out tomorrow morning.

With Thomas now out of danger, she decided to leave going to the hospital until the afternoon. The cottage was fully equipped with a washing machine and tumble drier, and she spent the morning washing and ironing everything in sight.

She was glad to be busy, but at half past one she left Begonia Cottage, stopping on the way to buy magazines for Thomas and Camilla. When she got to Thomas's room, however, she discovered that she had no need to go along to Camilla's room. Camilla was visiting Thomas.

'How are you feeling?' Eden enquired generally of the two, who looked so happy with each other that she began to feel like an unwanted third.

'Fine,' Thomas smiled at Camilla.

'Both of us,' Camilla smiled at Thomas.

'This—er—is a permitted visit?' Eden asked, by now realising that the girl her stepbrother loved was not beyond commandeering a wheelchair and taking a tour of the hospital if she felt like it.

'Of course it is!' Camilla exclaimed, but she had to grin when she added, 'They've permitted me one hour. I shall, naturally, try to stretch that to two.'

'Naturally,' Eden grinned back. Looking from one to the other she asked, 'I've some shopping I should really like to do before the shops close—anything either of you need?'

She left Thomas's room realising that although she had a small shopping list for the two, neither needed anything but the other's company.

The items of shopping did not take long to purchase, but she felt unwilling to intrude on the precious time which Camilla and Thomas were sharing. Eden drove to the hill which she had twice visited before.

Minutes ticked into an hour as she sat on the bench she had once shared with Sterne. But no matter how long she sat there, that strange feeling of contentment she had known when he had been by her side eluded her. More minutes ticked by, but she still could not recapture the magic she had felt when she had been there with him.

Two hours after she had left the hospital, Eden went back. Just in case Camilla had managed to extend her visit for longer than the two hours she had hoped for, though, Eden went to her room first.

'How long did you manage?' she asked as she placed a collection of toiletries down on the bedside locker.

'An hour and twenty minutes,' Camilla laughed, as she promised, 'I'll extend it further tomorrow.'

Eden stayed talking with her for about half an hour, then she went to see Thomas, who revealed that already the staff had had him out of bed.

'There'll be no holding you at this rate!' she exclaimed.

'I should hope not,' he declared, and indeed, as Eden studied him closely, she could see a difference in him from yesterday.

It was just gone seven when she left the hospital building that evening. She was crossing the forecourt, when suddenly she was in the grip of shock. There, parked next to her car, was a Jaguar! A Jaguar which she would know anywhere!

Her heart started to pound at the idea that Sterne was so near, and as excitement surged within her, she just had to turn round looking for him.

Her eyes were on the hospital entrance when, just as if she had willed it, she saw the tall shape of Sterne come through the doors.

It was just her luck, she fretted, that, when there were quite a few people milling about, Sterne's eyes should straight away single her out and catch her looking at him. Though if he had been searching for only her, he couldn't have spotted her sooner!

Irritated with herself for that stupid thought, because since his car was parked next to hers it was the obvious direction for him to look, Eden was annoyed with herself on another front too. She'd had twenty-four hours to prepare for this meeting, and what had she prepared—nothing! But—he was coming over!

With barely seconds available to prepare something, Eden remembered the way they had parted. They had not been the best of friends then, she recalled, so she could hardly be expected to greet him like some long-lost relative. Realising that by having stood stock-still nearer to his car than her own she was already showing some kind of surprise, Eden thought she had found just the right aloof note when, managing to get in first, she asked coolly, 'What are you doing here?'

'Pretty much the same as you, I should imagine,' he drawled coldly.

'You must have left London before five,' Eden shrugged, as she moved away from his car.

'If it's of any interest,' floated over the top of their two vehicles, 'I left around lunch time.'

Comprehending that he must still be quite worried about Camilla to have taken another half-day off, Eden attempted another offhand shrug as she unlocked her car, and told him, 'Your concern over your ward's health is unfounded. I saw Camilla myself today—she's doing very well.'

'Too well!' he grunted. 'If you've seen her you've no doubt heard that she feels well enough to decide for herself which hospital she wants to recuperate in!'

Eden nodded, and got into her car. She played about with the controls, and by the time she had turned the key in the ignition, Sterne was driving out of the forecourt.

Instantly she cursed the pride which had lifted her on to her high horse and had made her the aloof-sounding person she had been. True, he hadn't come across as exactly the world's most amiable person either, but she could have been nicer to him. Had she been nicer to him, had she been less aloof, then he might have stayed talking a little longer.

Reversing out of her parking spot, Eden negotiated her car on to the road. Having been on a high plateau of suspense and hope waiting for Sterne to arrive, she suddenly hit the other extreme.

In the depths of despondency, she supposed Sterne would have booked into a hotel anyway regardless of her churlish attitude. She drove along, reckoning dully that her chances of actually bumping into him at the hospital tomorrow, or of actually seeing him again, were just about nil.

On the thought that she might never see him again, though, she was proved wrong. Eden had just turned into the lane where Begonia Cottage stood when she spotted the Jaguar. She had just drawn up behind it when she saw Sterne, overnight bag in his hand, emerge from his car.

Be nice to him, urged an inner voice as, her heart beating erratically, she turned off the ignition and stepped out of her car. There was some light in the darkness but, afraid she might break out into a beaming smile, Eden kept her head bent while she locked up the Metro.

When Sterne came and stood by her, though, and addressed her in his most disagreeable tone to date, she promptly lost her fear that she might break out into spontaneous smiles. She felt more like kicking him on the shins when he grunted tersely, 'Have you any objection to my taking up half the cottage?'

'Not if you can keep your hands to yourself!' she snapped aggressively, and brushed past him and was heading for the path to the cottage when he snarled,

'*Twice* that lucky you'll never be!'

She did not deign to answer, but went fuming down the path. The swine! she thought, enraged. The conceited, egotistical swine! Going straight to the kitchen, she set the kettle to boil while she made herself a plate of sandwiches. Sterne did not enter the kitchen so she assumed he had taken his bag upstairs.

Making a hot drink, Eden found a tray and loaded her sandwiches on to it. Let Sterne Parnell find himself something to eat, she thought, peeved. There was plenty for him to choose from—she hoped it choked him. On that happy thought she added her coffee to her tray and took it up to her room.

Half an hour later, she had cooled down and knew she did not mean anything of the sort. She spent the following half-hour fighting a silent battle about whether she should go downstairs to try to make her peace with him. She had a fine excuse, she realised, in that the sheets from his bed which she had washed and ironed were now reposing in the airing cupboard. The least she could do would be to go and tell him where his bed linen was!

Eden was almost on her way to the door when she thought back to how, only a short while ago, she had instructed herself to be nice to him. Look what had happened then! He had been in a pig of a mood and she was just not the type to be meek and mild in the face of slings and arrows.

She kept to her room when she realised that, if Sterne was still in the same mood, far from making her peace with him, they could end up worse enemies than they already were. Anyway, he wasn't helpless, it wouldn't take him two minutes to find some clean sheets for his bed.

She did not sleep well that night. She faced the wall that divided their two rooms and wanted more than ever to go to him to clear everything up. She wanted to tell him that he had no need to fear for Camilla because she had seen her with Thomas, and there was no mistaking the love that Thomas had for her. She wanted to tell him that he had no need to worry that Thomas was only after Camilla's fortune, because Thomas would soon inherit a fortune of his own. Basically, she wanted everything that impeded the possibility of her and Sterne being friends out of the way. There was one very big snag, though, to any action that might clear everything up.

By his very attitude, Sterne had shown that he didn't give a damn whether they were friends or not.

When Eden awoke on Saturday morning, she discovered that a sudden surge of pride was making her certain that she did not give a damn whether Sterne Parnell wanted to be friends or if he didn't.

Her resolve to show him a cool front, however, received a severe dent when, bathed and dressed, she went into the kitchen. Proof that Sterne was up and about before her lay in the fact that the teapot beneath the cosy he had covered it with was still hot. But that he had put the cosy on the teapot at all to keep the pot warm showed that Sterne did not feel *too* unfriendly towards her.

Eden poured herself a cup of tea and, drinking it at the dining-table, she gave her common sense a prod. The fact that Sterne had made an attempt to keep the tea warm meant not a thing, she realised, other than that he was above being petty-minded. Still, she was just wishing that she had been big enough to tell him where the clean sheets were last night when suddenly the door opened, and the man who had occupied most of her thoughts just lately came in.

'G-good morning,' she greeted him civilly; if her heart was racing nineteen to the dozen at just the sight of him, then she was going to be the only one to know it.

'Good morning,' he replied evenly in answer to her tentative olive branch, and, noting that she was taking her ease rather than standing up at the sink while she drank her tea, he further unbent to enquire, 'Not rushing off to the hospital this morning?'

Eden gave him a half-smile to show that she held no ill will. 'Thomas is out of his coma now,' she informed him, only then realising that if Camilla had not told him, then Sterne might not know—not that that fact appeared to bother him either way. Eden bit down a feeling of edginess at that thought, and she produced another half-smile as she added, 'Actually, with Thomas off the critical list, I don't have to hurry to see him any more.'

Sterne put some water in the kettle and set it to boil while he spooned some instant coffee into a cup. Eden warmed to him because he seemed in no rush to leave the kitchen, and she warmed to him even more when, with a half-smile of his own, he looked at her and remarked, '*Actually*, with Camilla doing her level best to provoke, I don't think I'm in any hurry to go to the hospital either.'

Eden laughed, she couldn't help it. Sterne's sense of humour always had had the power to reach hers. The kettle boiled and she watched, and enjoyed watching, as he made himself a cup of coffee. When suddenly he looked up from his task, she found that her tongue was running away with her.

'I'm sorry Camilla is being the way she is with you,' she said hurriedly, and discovered that all she had thought was bubbling to the surface as she went on, 'Just as I'm sorry, on my own behalf, that I—that I accused you of—of being responsible for Thomas's accident.'

Sterne took a careful sip of his coffee. 'You no longer think I'm to blame?' he questioned quietly.

Eden shook her head. 'Even though the car didn't belong to Thomas, he should have had the brakes attended to when they started to be faulty,' she said, and defended her stepbrother the best she could when she went on, 'Normally, of course, he would have seen to it that the vehicle he was borrowing was in tip-top condition, but he started to go out with Camilla and...'

'And had other things to think about?' Sterne suggested, and even though Eden did not like to see that his smile had departed, and that he now wore a dark look, it was important to her—now that she had got this far—to get it all said.

'Yes,' she agreed, 'he had other things to think about. He fell deeply in love with Camilla and...' Her voice petered out when scepticism was added to Sterne's expression. 'He does love her!' she said shortly, forgetting in face of his scepticism that the last thing she wanted to do was to argue with Sterne.

'Really!'

The scornful way that 'Really!' reached her ears caused Eden's aggression to rise another notch. 'Yes—really!' she snapped. 'Thomas is deeply in love with Camilla, and,' she went on heatedly, knowing full well what lay at the bottom of all this, 'he's no more interested in the fortune she'll inherit than...'

'Then why,' Sterne chopped her off abruptly, 'when I left him in no doubt that I objected most strongly to him paying suit to my ward—and would never consent to his marrying her,' he hammered home to make Eden furious, 'did he attempt to force my hand by compromising her by spending nights alone with her under this roof?'

Astonishment mingled with fury, and Eden sprang from her chair. She was aware that she could not defend Thomas over this particular issue, but she saw no reason not to show Sterne the other side of the coin.

'If Camilla has been compromised by staying overnight here with Thomas,' she said snappily, 'then the same could be said of me! I too, have been compromised—only by you!'

She had not felt in any way compromised, but she saw the stilled look of tension about Sterne as she finished speaking. She had no idea what was going on inside his head, but she was suddenly hypnotised by the piercing look in his sharp grey eyes. Very slowly then, very deliberately, he said, 'Are you suggesting that I—should offer—to marry you?'

For all of a split second she was ready to snatch the opportunity. But the totally unromantic expression on his face caused her to know in the next split second that Sterne would go into cardiac arrest if she told him that there was nothing she would like better. Which left her knowing that his slow, deliberate question had been meant as sarcasm only, as a sneer only—and that hurt!

'Heaven save me!' she exclaimed mockingly in the next split second. 'That *would* be a fate worse than death!' She saw his eyes narrow at her mocking tone, but the fact that he didn't like the treatment he meted out served back at him was the least of her worries. Her eyes were flashing out her dislike of him just then when, hurt, she taunted, 'I promise you, Sterne Parnell, that when I marry it will be to a man who won't have to think in advance—is she marrying me for my money!' For her sins, her taunt was repaid with another helping of pain.

'Unless the unfortunate wretch is exceedingly dim, he'll be in no doubt about that!' Sterne tossed back at her acidly.

Winded, Eden was too proud to show it. 'You hateful swine!' she hissed. 'I'll never forgive you for that!'

'That's bound to keep me awake nights!' Sterne said toughly, and as yet more hurt stung Eden, she was on the brink of losing control.

'Do you leave this cottage, or do I?' she challenged hotly. And in case he hadn't got the message, 'I've no intention of spending a single night more under the same roof as you!' she hissed.

'My God!' he snarled, his jaw thrust forward. 'Don't flatter yourself that I'm panting to deprive you of your precious virginity—I'm quite well aware that you're saving *that* to sell to the highest bidder!'

Eden had tried a couple of times to land a slap on the side of Sterne's face. This time she succeeded. Furiously her hand flew through the air and she struck him a perfectly aimed blow. The stinging of her right hand nullified the pain in her heart, but only for a moment. And in that moment, Sterne had taken both her wrists in a grip of steel. She saw a pulse throb in his temple, and as he drew her to him, she feared that in his anger he intended to punish her mouth with his own. But she couldn't allow that. Weak where he was concerned, she feared that if he began to kiss her he would soon know of her weakness, and that would be her final humiliation.

'Don't you dare touch me!' she screamed when in one movement he let go of her wrists and hauled her up in his arms. With furious energy she struggled to be free, but his arms were like iron bands around her, and as his head started to come down, she panicked. In that panic, she screamed out the biggest lie of all. 'Oh God, how I *hate* you, Sterne Parnell!' she cried.

His mouth was so close she could feel his breath on her cheek. But, when she knew that it was too late, all at once his arms fell from around her. Suddenly she was free!

Rocking where she stood, she saw that Sterne was white-faced. Then he had swung abruptly about, and she could not see his face at all. Nor could she see him, for he had gone striding from the room.

Eden was in a state of shock about what had flared up, but she recognised the sound of him going up the stairs. She had not moved an inch when she heard him come down again and go striding to the front door. The front door opened, and there was something very final in the way he slammed it shut behind him.

She didn't hate him, she knew she didn't, but Eden did not regret that she had told him she did. She went up to her room and sat down on her bed, her arms crossed in front of her. She was in love with Sterne—nothing, it seemed, would change that—but it would be too painful to see him again.

She had no idea how long she sat hugging her arms defensively to her as though to ward off more pain. But when she eventually stood up, Eden had worked out what she was going to do.

First she tidied up her room. Next she tidied up the bathroom and packed her toothbrush and paste away. Most of the clothes she had brought were hanging in the wardrobe. She packed only what she thought Camilla would not require. She was passing Sterne's bedroom on her way to tidy the kitchen when her wish that Mrs Fox should have nothing to complain of made her halt to check that everything was as it should be in his room.

Everything was in order, and, to endorse that he had no intention of coming back to the cottage, Eden saw that he had left his key to the front door down on the dressing-table. She picked the key up and hurried to the kitchen.

Quickly she rinsed and put away the crockery which she and Sterne had used. And as the feeling that she would break down if she didn't get out of Begonia Cottage started to overcome her, she quickly grabbed up her belongings and made for the front door.

Mrs Fox was quite agreeable when Eden knocked at the adjoining cottage and asked if she could pay rent on Begonia Cottage for a further month. 'I have to go back to London,' she explained and, forcing a bright smile, she added, 'I think Miss Rodgers may well be allowed to leave hospital before my stepbrother, in which case she'll want to be as near to him as she can.'

'Of course she will,' Mrs Fox agreed, and as Eden handed the two keys into her safekeeping, Mrs Fox volunteered to see that the cottage was kept warm and aired ready for Miss Rodgers's return.

Having said goodbye to Mrs Fox, Eden drove to the nearest phone box. Cowardly she might be but, yesterday's hope turned completely on its head, she just could not run the risk of bumping into Sterne at the hospital. With Camilla now able to visit Thomas each day, though, Eden could see no reason why she should run that risk. Eden knew that Thomas held her in the same regard she held him, but the only person he really wanted to see was his Camilla.

Eden came away from the phone box wondering at the liar she had become since knowing Sterne Parnell. For, although there was nothing wrong with her but a heart that felt as though it had been beaten to a pulp, she had just told the Sister in charge of Thomas that she thought she was going down with a cold. She had asked her to pass on the message that rather than risk infecting him, and possibly the whole hospital, she had decided not to visit for a couple of days. From the phone box, she drove straight to London.

A month was to pass before Eden returned to the Lake District. A month in which she had no spirit or will to do anything, but because one day spent in fretting and moping about Sterne did not make her feel an atom better, Eden made a conscious effort to pick up the threads of her life.

The day after her flight from Begonia Cottage, she wrote to her stepbrother and lied on paper. She embroidered on the invention of her cold, telling him that although she felt well enough in herself, she had returned to London, and would stay in London until she thought she was completely germ-free.

In the clutches of depression when she went to bed at night, Eden woke up depressed. A few days later, she took a glance around the awful flat, and knew that she had to get out. At three o'clock that afternoon she booked into a small, family-run hotel.

She wrote again to Thomas the following day and perjured her soul some more by telling him that, what with her cold and the dampness of the flat, she had not been able to get warm. She had therefore moved to the stated new temporary address. She added that she was much better, but as she intended to spend every waking moment searching for a more permanent abode, she might not be able to get up to see him.

Then she began an assault of the estate agents. By the end of that week, though, she and her car had gone miles, but without success.

Fear of bumping into Sterne if she went north hospital-visiting kept Eden in London on Sunday. It was ridiculous, and she knew it was ridiculous, that when her heart ached for a sight of him, she was doing her best to keep out of his way. All the same she still felt enough concern for her stepbrother to want to ring the hospital and check that he was maintaining his progress.

Before she could do that, however, her stepbrother rang her. 'Thomas!' she exclaimed in delight when the daughter of the hotel put the call through to her room. 'I was going to ring... How are you?' she broke off to ask. 'How's Camilla?'

'How's your cold?' he asked in return.

'It's as though I'd never had one,' Eden replied, slightly ashamed.

'Good,' Thomas said warmly, and went on to tell her that he and Camilla were making rapid progress, so much so in Camilla's case that they were allowing her home next week.

'She's coming back to London!' Eden exclaimed.

'No way!' he replied. 'She's going to stay at Begonia Cottage. Thanks for paying the extra rent, by the way.'

'You've seen Mrs Fox?''

'She's been in to see us both several times,' Thomas said, adding, 'She's turned out to be something of a gem.'

'She has?' Eden enquired, and heard that Mrs Fox had instantly volunteered her services when she knew that Camilla was coming out of hospital.

'She said that since she cooks a meal for herself in the evening she can just as easily cook for two, and since she's out in her car most days, she can give Camilla a lift to visit me.'

'That's—good,' Eden told him quietly, but she felt compelled to ask, 'Do you think I should come up and stay with Camilla while she's convalescing?'

'Can't see much point in that really, love,' he replied to her intense relief. 'Camilla will be here visiting me most of the time, and on the occasions when Mrs Fox can't ferry her, there's a more than adequate taxi service, I'm told. Besides,' he went on with a smile in his voice, 'from what you said in your letter, you haven't got time to do anything but house-hunt. Have you found what you're looking for yet?'

What Eden was looking for more than a permanent dwelling was peace of mind. When Thomas rang off she knew that, while Sterne Parnell continued to dominate her thoughts, peace of mind was something she would never find.

Thomas phoned several times over the next few weeks, and Eden was always pleased to hear from him. But although he spoke a lot about Camilla, never once did he mention her guardian. Eden was burning to hear the smallest snatch of anything about Sterne, but she could not bring herself to ask about him.

She had been back in London for four weeks exactly when Thomas rang again. From the joy she heard in his voice, Eden knew that something pretty wonderful had happened.

'They're letting you out?' she guessed, once their greetings were over.

'Next Tuesday,' he said excitedly. 'But Thursday's much more important than Tuesday.'

Eden fell for it. 'What happens on Thursday?' she asked.

'Thursday is the day that Camilla and I get married!' Thomas announced.

'Married!'

Eden was still gasping when he affectionately revealed how Camilla, taking advantage of him being a captive audience, had beavered away to convince him that only an idiot would believe he was responsible for his father's past.

'What really got me, though,' he confessed, 'was when Camilla said that if I didn't mind ruining my own life and happiness over a man I had no recollection of, did I think it right that her life and happiness should be ruined through him too? Had not, in fact, enough criminal harm been done by my father, without me adding to it?'

Eden was smiling as she told him, 'Camilla was only speaking the truth, but I'm so glad she got you to see sense.'

'Me too, now that I think of it,' he replied, and she knew that he was grinning his head off. Her smile had disappeared, however, when a moment later he insisted, 'Now you *are* coming to our wedding, aren't you, Eden? We aren't getting married until twelve-thirty, so if you don't want to lose two days' house-hunting by coming up on Wednesday, you could start out early on Thursday, and be here in plenty of time.'

'I'll—er—do that, I think,' she replied slowly, dreadfully torn between wanting to see her stepbrother married and wanting to be a million miles away if Sterne was attending too. Quite desperately then did she need to know whether or not he was going to be there. 'Sterne...' she said, and she had to cough to clear a sudden constriction, but the 'he'll be there?' that she meant to ask would not leave her, and the question that she did ask was, 'Camilla's guardian—he'll—have—er—given his consent, of course?'

'Camilla doesn't need anyone's consent to be married,' Thomas replied. 'Not now that she's had her eighteenth birthday.'

Eden collapsed into a chair after his call. She could not have been more pleased at the happy news that Camilla and Thomas were getting married on Thursday, but thoughts of Sterne were soon at the forefront of her mind again.

When Monday arrived she was no further forward in knowing whether Sterne would be there now that he was no longer Camilla's guardian. Just in case, though, she did not go home-hunting that day. Instead, she spent that Monday in searching the shops for something to wear on Thursday.

She had searched the shops on Tuesday too, and as she set off early for the Lake District two days later, she was pleased with her efforts. October had given way to November, and the fine wool of her deep apricot-coloured skirt with its matching matador-style jacket was just the thing for the occasion and the weather. With her two-piece, Eden had teamed a deep cream-coloured wool blouse. Her newly washed white-blonde hair fell straight to her shoulders, and was topped by a deep cream fine wool beret which she wore at a classic angle.

Eden had not expected Sterne to stay out of her head as she drove, nor did he. She thought of the way they had parted, and of the awful things he had said to her. Though, she recalled, she hadn't been backward in that department herself. She had told him that she would never forgive him, and that she hated him, and... Suddenly Eden was remembering again why she had told Sterne she would never forgive him. It was his view that when she married there would be no doubt that she would be marrying for money... All at once then she found she was wondering if Thomas had been in touch with Sterne. Had Thomas told him that neither of them would find it necessary to marry for money? Did Sterne in fact know that there was a middle bit to her name? Did he know that her name was Eden Glendening-Smith? Did the name Glendening-Smith mean anything to him? she wondered, as her car sped northwards. As a businessman, Sterne must have heard of her father.

Eden was pulling up outside Begonia Cottage when she realised that it would not affect anything anyway. She was in love with Sterne, but although he had once desired her, and had shown her kindness a couple of times, that did not amount to love returned.

She sighed as she got out of the car and faced the fact that in the long weeks since she had last seen him, she'd had ample time to cool down and to know that she loved him enough to forgive his remarks ten times over. It was pride-bruising, though, to have to accept that in the short weeks since he had last seen her, he had probably not given her another thought.

Nevertheless, her heart was pounding as she knocked on the door of Begonia Cottage. She had seen no sign of the Jaguar, but that did not mean to say he was not around.

'Eden!' Thomas cried gladly, as he pulled open the door. As they hugged each other Camilla appeared and joined in the embrace.

'Neither of you look as if there was ever anything the matter with you!' Eden exclaimed when in the sitting-room she had the chance to observe the pair fully.

'Thomas's doctor said that he's got to go a bit carefully to start off with,' said Camilla, and sounded so protective of him that Eden smiled and understood how much she loved him.

There was half an hour to spare before they went to the church, but while Eden did not think it would cast a blight on proceedings if she asked Camilla 'Will your ex-guardian be present?' she just could not ask.

Camilla and Thomas kept up a lively flow of conversation, which she joined in while at the same time she strained her ears for the sound of the Jaguar. When a knock sounded on the door, she very nearly leapt out of her skin, and as Camilla and Thomas left the room to answer it, she again kept her ears pitched—this time for the loved sound of Sterne's deep-timbred voice.

But the voice she heard was that of a female, and as Camilla and Thomas returned with Mrs Fox in tow, Eden went over to shake hands with her.

'Mrs Fox thinks it would be more seemly if Camilla and I went to the church in separate cars,' Thomas stated. 'Will you take me, Eden, while Mrs Fox takes Camilla?'

'With pleasure,' Eden beamed, but her heart was somewhere down in her boots. All too plainly, Sterne was not expected.

Even so, as they trooped out to the two cars Eden was still tempted to ask if he would be there. She would have welcomed being put out of the misery of expecting to see him at any moment. Love, she confessed to herself as Thomas gave directions to the church and she drove off, had made a nonsense of her. Far from never wanting to see Sterne again, she now wanted to see him more than anything!

She and Thomas were at the church and had just got out of the car when, as if defying her to suppress it any longer, Sterne's name came blurting out from between her lips.

'Sterne...' she began, and when Thomas looked at her, she had to go on, 'Sterne Parnell,' she said, but she still could not ask if he would be there, 'er—you've let him know about your inheritance?'

His answer was to endorse what Eden already knew—that Thomas cared little about money. 'It wasn't until yesterday that I thought to tell Camilla about it,' he replied.

'Dream!' she teased.

For a brief while during the marriage ceremony she managed not to think about Sterne. Camilla looked lovely in a white dress she had purchased especially for the occasion, and as she exchanged vows with Thomas, Eden had difficulty in holding back a tear. Thomas was a dear man, and as he looked adoringly at Camilla, Eden could not help but think how happy and proud the parents would have been of him if they'd been alive to see this day.

When the ceremony was over, Eden and Mrs Fox went to act as witnesses. Amid happy congratulations they adjourned to a hotel recommended by Mrs Fox for the wedding lunch. It was a merry meal, but as it drew to a close, Eden thought she had glimpsed a trace of strain on her stepbrother. Mindful of Camilla's warning that Thomas still had to go carefully, Eden refused more coffee.

'I wouldn't mind being on my way before it gets dusk,' she excused, pretending not to see that it was still a bright sunlit day outside.

'I hate driving any distance in the dark,' Mrs Fox opined, and offered with a cheerful smile, 'If you're not coming back to the cottage, I'll see to it that Mr and Mrs Morrisey get back home safely.'

Everyone laughed as Camilla realised that she was the Mrs Morrisey referred to, and Eden told them she thought she'd start off directly.

'I'll ring you in the week,' Thomas told her as they parted.

'You concentrate on getting really well,' she replied.

Eden was in sober spirits as she drove away from the hotel. Sterne, oh, Sterne, she grieved. She had so wanted to see him, but he hadn't been there.

Her route took her near to the hospital, and on a stretch of road she knew Eden fell to wondering—had Sterne not been at the wedding because he hadn't been invited? Did he even know that Camilla was being married today?

She drove past the hospital without really noticing it, her thoughts taken up with Sterne. Perhaps he did know about the wedding but was upset that now that Camilla was eighteen, she no longer had to seek his permission about anything and could, in fact, marry anyone she chose?

Her head was still full of Sterne, any pain he felt her pain, when Eden suddenly realised that she was not on the road she had meant to travel on. All at once she became aware that she had taken a detour and was in fact within an ace of reaching the hill which Sterne had introduced her to.

Eden remembered the very first time she had gone there. She had found tranquillity—a certain peace—*and*, she vividly recalled, she had felt that Sterne had liked her.

Just as she ached to feel tranquil again, so she ached to feel at peace within herself, and she was drawn more than ever towards the hill. She overlooked the fact that she had not found inner contentment the last time she had been there, and she motored closer. Somehow she felt compelled to keep on going and not to turn about.

The sun was still shining when Eden parked. Tossing off her smart beret, she left her vehicle and, shrugging into her car coat, she observed how most of the trees had shed their leaves and how, despite the weak sun rays, the ground looked damp and most unsuitable for her shoes. But that something that was calling her on would not be denied.

Being careful not to slip on the leafy ground, Eden started to climb the small hill, and she reached the top to look down to the valley sprawled out below. The scene was already etched in her mind, but again she took in the trees to the right of her, the hilly clump to her left, and she let her eyes wander to the bench where she and Sterne had once sat. She remembered the empathy she had felt between them at that time, and as if magnetised by the bench, she started down the slope towards it.

She was in the middle of recalling how Sterne had held glances with her when seated together on that very bench, and had declared, 'Life—is full of surprises', when she halted mid-step. For something in the trees to the right of her had moved and, staggering her completely, a moment later a tall, dark-haired man had appeared. Not believing her eyes, Eden was still dumbstruck when the man spotted her and, as he did, so he too stopped dead in his tracks.

She was half-way between the bench and the top of the hill, and she was doing her best to recover, when all her instincts urged her to take flight. But Sterne had not moved, and she guessed he was coolly waiting to observe what she would do. With her heart drumming she remembered that harsh way they had parted, and she thought she could be forgiven if she cold-shouldered him, turned about and, without a word to him, went back to her car.

Against that, though, was the fear that Sterne—purely for awkwardness's sake, of course—might come after her to question what she was doing there and might perceive her inner turmoil and wonder at it!

Pride moved her a few more steps towards the bench, and as she moved her fast-racing heart suddenly set up the most uproarious clamouring. For Sterne too had had the choice of turning about and of giving her the cold shoulder, but he too had moved, and his footsteps were heading in the same direction as hers!

As ever—they were on a collision course!

CHAPTER NINE

STERNE had more ground to cover than Eden, but with his longer strides, they reached the bench at the same time. They stopped about two yards away from each other, but that was quite close enough for her to read in his unsmiling expression that he had not thawed towards her since their last meeting.

Her heart was beating painfully within her as she matched her cool front to his. Dearly did she wish she had gone back to her car and driven off. But it was too late now to wish that pride had not prevented her from running away. Sterne, she observed, seemed to have no wish to speak to her, but he appeared content to just stand looking at her and to wait for her to speak first. It could, she supposed, have been his pure common courtesy, but she knew it wasn't, and she felt a familiar burst of adrenalin—which had been notably absent since the last time she had seen him.

'You didn't make it?' she snapped, her voice more accusatory than questioning. Through stormy blue eyes she saw him rock slightly back on his heels.

'Make what?' he drawled, to add to her crossness with him.

'The wedding!' she replied shortly. 'Camilla and Thomas were married today!' she blurted out, the angry words leaving her before she could remember that Sterne might not have known beforehand. But it was too late then for her to decide that perhaps she might have acquainted him with that piece of news more tactfully, for he was again sending her adrenalin soaring.

'So, you've come to gloat!' he accused cuttingly.

'No, I haven't!' she erupted, but she was at a loss to know how to answer him when he promptly shot at her:

'Then what are you doing here?'

Her mind was suddenly a blank. 'I...' she began, and had not the smallest truth or falsehood in her head to help her out. 'I...' she said again, and was suddenly released from her brain numbness. 'I didn't know you'd be here, did I?' she tossed at him tartly and, not giving him time to answer, she managed to pull herself together enough to challenge, 'For that matter, what are *you* doing here?'

It would have been fantasy to expect Sterne to be stuck for an answer, for she had never caught him without one yet. But, albeit the answer he gave was not a direct answer to the question she asked, Eden was so stunned by his reply that she did not notice it.

'I've been to see Camilla married,' he told her.

'B-but you weren't there—at the church!' she gasped, wide-eyed.

His eyes fastened on the brilliant blue of hers. 'I was,' he replied coolly.

'But—I—we... None of us saw you!' Eden was still gasping, but as the thought again struck that he might be upset that he could do nothing about Camilla marrying whomsoever she chose, so the cool front she wanted to show him started to evaporate. 'Y-you couldn't bring yourself to come over and wish Camilla all happiness for her future with Thomas?' she asked softly, and felt as if Sterne had physically touched her when his glance left her eyes, went down to her gentle mouth, and back again.

'I should spoil her wedding day?' he questioned, the mere fact that some of his cool tone was missing warming Eden. 'The way Camilla regards me just now,' he said evenly, his eyes now steady on hers, 'she was happier to think of me not being there.'

Eden knew that he spoke only the truth, but it hurt her that—for all he faced the issue without illusion—he might be hurt. 'But Camilla *did* contact you to tell you that she was being married today?' She sought for some way to soften what might have been hard for him to swallow. Sterne shaking his head told her she was wasting her time trying to ease things for him.

She looked past him but barely noticed the view. She moved her position slightly, unconsciously bringing Sterne's attention to her elegantly but, in this instance of standing on a leafy hillside, unsuitably clad feet.

'Why not take advantage of this bench to enjoy your view,' he suggested, and to make her heart all out of step again, he moved to come and take hold of her arm and, just as though he was *not* wishing to see the last of her, he guided her to the dry seat with its dry leaf-free concrete base.

Eden's heart pounded more than ever when, as if to prove that he was in no particular hurry, Sterne came and sat down beside her. She was aware then that if she wasn't careful her imagination would take over. Sterne had an eye for the picturesque too, which was why he had come here that first time. After a week spent within the confines of his office, what else would he do but take advantage when possible of being out in the open air for as long as he could?

Having given herself a short, speedy lecture, Eden decided that since she had only just sat down, she could hardly bob straight up again and say she was going. She decided to give it a minute or two before she said her final goodbye to Sterne. She had to think hard, though, in those few minutes of pretending to be looking at the view, to try to remember where they had left their conversation.

He had known, she recalled, without Camilla telling him, that she was being married today. That meant that somebody else had let him know. Eden knew then that Sterne had asked or paid someone to keep their ear to the ground about Camilla's doings. She knew too that at one time that realisation would have made her angry. But she could not feel angry with Sterne. A tenderness seemed to be in charge of her to think that he had come all this way to see his ex-ward married, but because he had known it would ruin her day to see him, he had taken great care to see, but not be seen.

Suddenly then, Eden knew that she had to tell him everything about her stepbrother. Nothing she said could harm Thomas, but if Sterne was tasting the bitterness of believing that he had failed in his guardianship—even if Camilla was no longer his ward—then Eden knew she just *had* to tell him.

'Sterne!' she turned to him on sensitive impulse, and met his grey eyes full on. 'About . . .' she began, but she had started off badly and, trying to get it all said at once, she told him quickly, 'You've no need to worry that Thomas has married Camilla for her fortune . . .' She faltered when she saw a coolness enter the eyes that were fixed to hers. 'In January, Thomas will be twenty-five,' she resumed, determined to finish what she had started, 'and when he's twenty-five, he'll inherit a fortune of his own.'

Any pleasure she felt to have relieved Sterne's mind on the subject of Thomas being a fortune-hunter was gone when Sterne soon poured cold water on her tender vibrations, and consequently made her angry.

'His fortune is no doubt at present waiting for him in a numbered account in some Swiss bank,' he said acidly, adding bluntly, 'From choice, I'd prefer that Camilla doesn't touch a penny of Morrisey's inheritance!'

Abruptly Eden got to her feet. She was furious with Sterne and her miserable fate that she seemed destined to part from him in anger. Fire was flashing in her eyes when, as he rose to his feet too, she flung at him, 'If you weren't so hasty to jump to conclusions, you might learn something!'

Ready to charge up the hill and down the other side, Eden had moved her right foot but one pace when Sterne's right hand shot out and clamped down on her shoulder. Seconds, long, endless seconds passed before, having stayed her, he asked, 'What—might I learn, Eden?'

'Th-the truth,' she said huskily, and was once again stumped to know what to say next.

Especially when, as if he was giving her the benefit of all doubt, when at one time there had been no doubt in his mind about her or her stepbrother, Sterne said quietly into her ear, 'I'm always interested in the truth.'

Eden supposed that having his hand on her shoulder, his face so close to hers, must have unnerved her a little more. Because, when she had no intention of returning to the wooden bench, she discovered that the wooden bench was where she was. Only as Sterne's hand left her shoulder and he reseated himself beside her did she come to her full senses to realise that he had guided her back to where she had sprung up from!

She tried hard for some smart remark, but when she realised that he was waiting to hear some truth from her, the only smart thing she could find to say was a feeble, if disparaging, 'Born-again listener!' Strangely, though, Sterne did not rise to her sarcasm but, stranger still, now seemed the epitome of patience as he waited—for her to put her money where her mouth was, so to speak. 'You got it all wrong,' she told him.

'I don't see how,' he replied in clipped tones. 'If Morrisey didn't want to marry Camilla he showed a marked lack of direction today. If...'

'Of course he wanted to marry her!' Eden felt herself growing angry again. 'I meant...'

'Are you saying that I was misinformed?' Sterne cut in again. 'Are you saying that Morrisey's father was not the crook the records prove he was? Are you...'

'Oh, shut up!' Eden swung round in her seat, and seeing that Sterne had one arrogant eyebrow raised aloft at her rudeness, she was entirely unrepentant. But, even so, she was forced to qualify when Sterne did 'shut up' and said not another word, 'Perhaps you didn't get it *all* wrong, just—most of it.'

Watching Sterne, she saw that he looked as though he might have something to say, something in antagonistic opposition to her statement. Something argumentative anyway, she thought. But he must have swallowed it down, whatever it was, because to her surprise, all he said was, 'Carry on—what exactly did I get wrong?'

Looking at him levelly, she tried to assess how ready he was to hear her out. Somehow, though, just looking at the face of the only man she wanted to be with seemed to sap her of all her aggression. So it was quietly that she said, 'You've jumped to too many conclusions where Thomas and I are concerned. You did it again just now when you decided that the money Thomas is due to inherit came from his father.'

Eden could see that she had surprised Sterne this time, but his eyes were steady on hers when he enquired, 'His inheritance comes from some other relative?'

'In a way,' she replied. 'From my father, actually.'

'*Your* father!'

She started to feel more comfortable when she observed that, though slightly incredulous, Sterne seemed more wanting to believe her than ready to dismiss everything she told him as blatant lies.

'My father,' she nodded, and neither wanted to hurt Sterne nor gloat, so she tried to soften what she wanted to tell him by saying first, 'The information you had about Thomas's father must have been at the forefront of your mind when you came to the flat looking for Camilla when she ran away. So it's—er—understandable, I suppose, that when I told you that Thomas was my stepbrother, that you should assume that his father was my stepfather, when in actual fact . . .'

'He wasn't!'

Eden shook her head. 'It was the other way around,' she said, and when she saw that Sterne looked faintly staggered, she went quickly on to tell him, 'Thomas's mother had divorced her husband some years previously when my widowed father met her. They fell in love, and married.' Her voice started to fade, and it was quietly that she added, 'They both died earlier this year.'

She saw a moment of compassion cross Sterne's face, but he was keeping strictly to the point, and was being most careful not to be accused of leaping to further conclusions when, as if viewing what she was telling him with some importance, he detailed slowly, 'So, *your* father became Morrisey's stepfather, and when he died, he left his stepson a fortune?' His look was suddenly unrelenting when, as though afraid she was leading him on some false trail, he asked harshly, 'Your father was a wealthy man?'

'Yes, to both questions,' Eden replied. 'Thomas will claim his inheritance when he's twenty-five. And my father was a very successful businessman.'

Sterne had no further question to ask for some minutes, but Eden was certain that his brain was at work dissecting all she had told him. Oddly, though, when she had thought his next question would be on the subject of either Thomas or her father, it was not. And had she not known better, she would have thought that Sterne had more interest in her than he had in either her step-brother or her father, because when his next question came, it was a question about her. But Eden did know better. She had already owned that being in love with Sterne had made a nonsense of her, so there was no way in which she was going to believe in the imaginings of her head.

'So,' Sterne began again, 'where does Eden Smith come into all this?'

'I don't come into it anywhere,' she replied as evenly as she could. 'I merely happen to be Thomas's step-sister, as I told you. I love him like the brother I never had, and I want him to be happy. And,' she added, just a shade defiantly, 'I'm sure that with Camilla he *will* be very happy!'

Sterne grunted, but even though Eden had introduced Camilla into the conversation, it seemed that he did not want to talk about his ex-ward either.

'And your name—it really is Smith?' he enquired, his eyes still on her.

'Yes,' Eden replied, and tacked on, 'It's a bit of a mouthful, but if you want all of it, it's Eden Glendening-Smith.'

'Glendening-Smith!' Sterne exclaimed, and she saw from his taken-aback look that he knew of one other by the same surname. 'Oh, God!' he said on a half-groan. 'The vile things I said about you being on the make weren't made to a relative of Vaughan Glendening-Smith, were they?'

'I don't suppose it's all that often that you shoot yourself in the foot,' Eden grinned, but she was without a smile when she asked, 'Did you know my father?'

'Oh, hell!' muttered Sterne. 'He was your father?' Eden nodded, and had to wait while he swallowed on that information, before he revealed, 'I met him occasionally at various business functions. His wizardry in the world of finance is still spoken of in the City. But,' he was soon back to asking questions about her, 'I never heard so much as a mention that he had a daughter!'

Looking at Sterne, Eden could see nothing in his expression to suggest that he thought she was making the whole of it up. And, heartily relieved that he at last seemed ready to trust her word without question, she was able to answer him openly.

'I think my father must have kept quiet about his family on purpose. Only recently have I fully understood why,' she confided. 'Obviously he knew all about Thomas's father, but he didn't want Thomas to be placed in the limelight where someone might tell him the truth about his father's criminal activities.'

'Your stepbrother didn't know of his father's career of crime!' Sterne asked, looking shaken.

'Not until you told him of it,' Eden replied. 'He thought, as I did, that his father had died soon after his mother divorced him,' she added, and saw that Sterne seemed too stunned for words, for many long seconds passed before, to make her heart pound furiously, he exclaimed softly,

'Oh my dear, dear Eden! How I've wronged you! How I've wronged you both.'

Eden almost melted at the sincerity in his eyes, and at the heart-stopping thrill it gave her to hear him call her his dear. But common sense was soon leaping in to give her some stiffening, and again she knew she must not let her imagination take over. Sterne calling her his dear meant nothing more than that he was very truly sorry for his actions.

That thought put her on an even keel again, and she followed it through to the natural question, 'You don't, then, hold it against Thomas—about his father?'

'What sort of a bigot do you think I am?' Sterne asked shortly, but, nothing wrong with his memory, 'Don't answer that!' he said quickly, adding, 'I've nothing against Morrisey—now I know the facts about...'

'But you had everything against him before you knew the facts?' Eden cut in. 'Before you knew he wasn't a fortune-hunter?' Conversely, she could only love Sterne the more when he did not try to pretend that it had been other than the way it had been.

'I handled it badly,' he owned, and as though searching for her understanding, he looked deeply into her eyes and explained, 'Camilla was twelve years old when I so willingly took on her guardianship. But even at twelve she was a wilful baggage. I had no particular problems while she was at boarding school,' he went on, 'but when she drew near to marriageable age, I began to realise how great was the responsibility I had accepted.'

'Because of the fortune she would inherit on her wedding day?'

Sterne nodded. 'I owed it to her father to do my very best. In short, before I'd ever heard of your stepbrother I was already envisaging difficulties over fortune-hunters. In advance,' he told her wryly, 'I was prepared to treat any suitor for her with the utmost suspicion.'

'Which is why you hired a firm of private detectives to look into Thomas's background,' Eden put in, quite unable to feel angry with him as she accepted, and even began to admire him for not treating his guardianship of Camilla lightly.

'I shouldn't have dispensed with their services when I did,' Sterne replied.

'You shouldn't?'

'Had I not done so they would have dug deeper and most likely have revealed that Camilla's suitor was shortly to inherit a considerable sum of his own. As it was, I waited only to receive the report about Morrisey's father when I decided that I could deal with the matter myself from then on—I certainly did that,' he added heavily. 'They both ended up in hospital.'

'They both ended up happily married—to each other,' Eden put in quickly. With Sterne having done a complete about-turn, she was ready to find every excuse for him. 'It wasn't your fault that the car Thomas was borrowing wasn't in a road-worthy condition.' Suddenly she became aware that Sterne was looking at her as though her defence of him was something he had not expected, 'And anyway,' she said quickly, as she searched for cover, 'what with finding out about Thomas's father and everything, you had Camilla to protect. You must have thought we were down on our uppers when you called at the flat and saw the crummy conditions we were living in,' she added for extra cover.

'You were borrowing the flat, I think you said,' Sterne recalled.

'Our own home had been sold,' Eden told him, and explained, 'Because of my stepmother's chronic bronchitis, my father decided that we should live in the Bahamas. The parents had left on the first leg of their journey when they had a car accident which...' her voice became chokey '...took both their lives,' she ended.

Her eyes had misted over, and she looked down at her hands. But suddenly Sterne had sent all held-back tears from her, because, in the empathy of the moment, one of his hands had come out to take hold of hers.

'Poor Eden,' she heard him say gently, 'no wonder you were near to collapse when I told you of your step-brother's accident. The other accident must have been brought vividly back to you.'

Somehow Eden had not expected Sterne to remember the way she had been when, at that hotel, he had come and told her how the police had been in touch with his housekeeper. 'Well...' she said as she struggled to get herself back together, which was difficult while Sterne still held her hands, 'it's all in the past now. Thomas and I went to London when the new people moved into our old home. Then Thomas met someone he'd been at school with who offered us the use of his flat while he was away. Neither of us knew how awful it was until we got there, but in those early days of losing the parents and looking around for somewhere to buy, we had bigger things to be upset about than living in a grotty flat—the awfulness of the flat seemed the least of our worries.'

Sterne's hand coming to help his other hand to enclose both of hers made Eden feel weak at the knees. She knew then that it was time she said her goodbyes to him. But first, she was weak enough to want to stay just a moment longer.

'You're still looking for somewhere permanent to live?' he asked gently.

She nodded, hoping he had not spotted how she'd had to swallow from emotion at his gentleness with her. 'When Thomas fell in love with Camilla and asked her to marry him, I started to look for somewhere for just myself.'

'You haven't found anywhere yet?' Sterne asked, and at that something indefinable in his voice, Eden looked up to find that she was gazing into the warmest pair of grey eyes.

Immediately her heart went out of gear and she found something of the greatest of interest over his shoulder. She knew then, as she dismissed the fact that he should have a warm look for her as a pure figment of her imagination, that she must not stay a moment more. Her imagination was getting out of hand.

'Not yet,' she said brightly. Firmly she pulled her hands back out of his grasp. 'But I've moved out of the flat and, since I'm not too keen on impersonal hotels, I'm now living in a small and friendly family-run hotel until I can buy a place of my own. Which reminds me,' she said, as, realising that she was gabbling, she stood up, 'I've a property to view this evening when the vendors arrive home from work.'

Eden owned that she was already unnerved. She was unnerved even more when Sterne too stood up. She noticed that his expression was serious, and that he seemed keyed up, but any thought she might have had to stretch out a hand to shake hands with him in parting came to nought. For when it came to it, her hand seemed too paralysed to move towards him.

'Goodbye, Sterne,' she said abruptly, and turned hurriedly away.

She was at the other side of the bench when his voice halted her. 'Don't . . .' he said, and she thought his voice sounded strained and not like his voice at all, when, 'Don't—go!' jerkily reached her ears.

Blaming her imagination for inventing a note of strain in his voice which could not possibly be there, Eden wanted to go on in the direction she was facing. But, just as her right hand had seemed paralysed a minute earlier, so her legs now seemed paralysed, unable to take her away from him. She realised then that her subconscious must have joined in to make her stay to hear why Sterne did not want her to go.

Trying to banish her imagination along with her subconscious, Eden kept her back to Sterne as she decided that, since this was one of the few times that she was parting from him without animosity, perhaps he wanted to invite her to share a pot of tea somewhere. Though if that was the case, he was taking his time in getting his invitation out.

'I've told you,' she said over her shoulder, before he could ask any such thing, 'that I have to get back to...'

'Still hate me?' Sterne cut across her attempt to let him know that she did not have time for so much as a cup of tea.

His question was unexpected though, but, aside from remembering that she had once told him in no uncertain terms that she hated him, Eden thought she knew what the question was about. He was aware now of all she had *not* previously told him, so he must be asking if his actions against Thomas caused her still to hate him now that Thomas had his heart's desire and was married to Camilla.

'Hate you? No, I don't hate you,' she told him, and would have taken a step up the hill, only she discovered that Sterne had waited no longer than to hear her declare that she did not hate him when he had moved.

Light on his feet as ever, he had moved without her hearing him, and suddenly he had placed himself between her and the bench. The first Eden knew of his speedy movement was when a hand clamped on either of her arms, and Sterne was preventing her from taking so much as one small step more away from him.

'You don't hate me,' he said into her ear, 'but you do feel something for me, Eden?' She tried to shake her head, to deny it, whatever he was asking, but the whole of her being felt weak from just his nearness, and the partial paralysis she had experienced now seemed total. It was beyond her to shake her head to deny anything!

'You *do* feel something for me,' Sterne pressed, when she had not answered him. 'My memory of you in my arms tells me you're not immune to...'

'You're not being fair,' Eden cut him off quickly, in a sudden panic. While he had been asking of her hate in relation to everything that had happened to her step-brother, she could handle it. But when, unfairly, he made his question of her hate more personal—with Thomas playing no part in it—Eden knew herself to be much too vulnerable.

'To hell with being fair,' Sterne replied, and as his grip on her arms tightened, Eden had the oddest notion that he was taking a grip on himself too! Which *was* odd, she freely admitted. For, given that he drew a long and—as if he was about to chance his all—a slightly rocky breath, his question when it came seemed to her to be more obscure than chancey. 'Tell me,' he said, 'have you anything to inherit when you reach twenty-five?'

Eden exchanged vulnerability for bewilderment, and was happy to do so. She had no idea where Sterne's question was leading, but he had moved the conversation from the close personal track it had been on, and it was with a feeling of relief that she freely told him, 'Apart from some jewellery which I inherited straight away, the estate of the parents is divided down the middle. Like Thomas, I'm to receive my half on my twenty-fifth birthday.'

She had begun to relax a little, but she still had no idea what had prompted Sterne to ask the question he had. Suddenly though, some tension in him had communicated itself to her, and any feeling of being relaxed vanished as swiftly as it had arrived. Because the very next question which Sterne asked was a breath-stopping one.

'Would you then consider that I was only after your fortune—if, Eden—I asked you to marry me?'

For long moments, she was too much in shock to consider anything at all. And when she started to recover, she could not credit that she had heard the question she thought she had. But, given that Sterne's wealth probably made her inheritance small by comparison, the way in which his grip on her arms had intensified told her that he had asked her something which was pretty momentous for him too! He hardly seemed to be breathing, at any rate, as he waited for her answer. And all at once, Eden discovered that she had started to tremble, and that it was a trembling she could do nothing about. Even her voice, when she eventually found it, sounded shaky as she croaked,

'When I'm—twenty-five, do you m-mean?'

She would, she thought, in those moments of not being sure of anything save that there must be something very wrong with her hearing, have by far preferred to keep her back to Sterne. But he had other ideas. Slowly, inexorably, he began to move her. Slowly he moved her until she was turned about, and was facing him. And slowly it was that he placed firm fingers beneath her chin to tilt her head up.

Perhaps it was because she wanted to read whatever messages there were to be read in his eyes that Eden found the courage then to look at him. She discovered, though, that she was too confused by what was happening to know anything any more, for she could tell none of what Sterne was thinking from his eyes. Though what he was reading in hers must have given him some encouragement, she realised, for, even though he had to draw something of a shaky breath himself, it was firmly that he said,

'I can't wait three years, my dear. In fact,' he added, his voice thick in his throat as he held her eyes with his, 'if I dared to let myself believe half of what my intelligence is trying to tell me, I'd be hard put to it to wait three weeks—to make you my wife.'

Eden could see from his face that he was in deadly earnest, and her heart began to beat so violently within her that she had to open her mouth to breathe.

'W-what sort of—things—dare you not believe?' she asked chokily.

'I'm afraid to believe that your trembling means that, in some small way, you care for me,' Sterne replied as if he was having the same difficulty in breathing normally that she was having. 'I want to believe that the way in which your eyes are all big and kind of scared means that this moment has you too wondering where it will end. I want to put my arms around you, and tell you not to be scared, that everything's all right. But I'm too scared myself that I've got it all wrong to do anything that might have you spitting at me again that you hate me.'

Stunned by what she was hearing, Eden lost the use of her voice altogether, and feeling that she would faint if she did not sit down, she was much relieved when Sterne seemed to read how she was feeling. For he took her tenderly back to the bench and did not resume until they were seated once more.

'Instincts have been at work in me ever since I saw you halt on this hillside,' he told her then. 'Why, I've been asking and asking, did you drive off the route you should have taken, to come to this place? Why—when you hated me—were you attracted to this hillside where we had once sat together?' He paused and seemed to need to take a steadying breath before he could continue. 'You were saying goodbye when I began to dare to believe that maybe—just maybe—you had driven off your route for the same reason as I—because, despite what else was going on about us at the time, we were once happy here together for a short while.'

Eden swallowed a lump in her throat. 'You felt it too?'

Sterne nodded, but his eyes did not leave her face when, more tensed up than ever, he asked, 'Dare I believe that the fact that you're still here—with me—and haven't again shown a wish to go, could be further evidence that you're not rejecting my proposal out of hand?'

Never was Eden more glad that she was seated. She felt on the very brink of the most marvellous happening of her entire life. And yet, because it was so marvellous, so wonderful, it was at the same time painfully unbelievable. But all of what Sterne was saying, his expression, the look in his eyes, made her find the strength to face a most dreadful let-down, if let-down it be.

'You...' She had begun badly. She cleared her throat, and with a small nervous cough, she started off again. 'I...' she said this time, but that wasn't right either. 'Was...' she said, but she finally managed to complete the sentence, 'It—w-was a proposal, then?'

'Devil take your fortune, Eden,' Sterne told her promptly, 'it's you I want! I want, as I've never wanted—need, as I've never needed—to marry you!'

Warm colour seemed to suffuse every part of her at his words. 'You're in... You feel s-some—affection for me?' she managed huskily from her dry throat.

'Oh, my dear,' Sterne breathed tenderly, 'I'm half out of my mind about you.'

'You—are?' Eden whispered faintly, her eyes as large as saucers.

'For God's sake stop asking questions,' he grated suddenly, 'and tell me how you feel about me—if there's a chance...'

He did not have to finish. The look of utter strain on his face got through Eden's wonderment at all that was happening. He seemed a soul in torment, and, loving him, she could not take it.

'I'll marry you—if—if that's all right with you,' she told him, her voice betraying her nervousness that she still wasn't a hundred per cent sure that he truly meant what he said.

'That,' he answered, his hands coming to take her by the shoulders, 'is more than "all right" by me! Oh, my very dear Eden,' he breathed throatily and, as if words failed him, he drew her gently towards him and, placing the gentlest of kisses on her mouth, he looked deeply into her eyes—and seemed as if he too could not believe that what was happening had really come about. Then, as though the emotion in him was too much, he pulled her tenderly up against his heart.

Long, long moments ticked away, with Sterne finding comfort and contentment to have Eden where she so willingly was. On her part, Eden felt that she never wanted Sterne to let her go. Near his heart was where she wanted to be, for ever.

But, at length, just as if he had to see into her eyes once more, Sterne began to move her. She felt his lips on her hair, and his breath warm on her cheek. She looked up, straight into adoring grey eyes.

'I love you!' whispered Sterne. 'Oh, how I love you!' he breathed, and before Eden could begin to tell him how much she loved him, his head came down and, like a man starved for her, he kissed her.

Minutes passed while Eden, starved for him too, gave him kiss for kiss and gradually grew more confident that she was not going to wake up to discover that it had only been a dream.

'Love me?' Sterne asked when at last he pulled back to again look into her shining bright blue eyes and, by now, flushed cheeks. Feeling too full to speak, Eden nodded. 'For how long?' he wanted to know. 'When . . .'

'And you thought I asked a lot of questions?' Eden found her voice to gently tease, but she didn't have to stray far into her memory to be able to tell him, 'I realised some time ago that you had the power to affect my emotions from the very first moment of our meeting.'

'You wanted to hit me,' recalled Sterne affectionately.

'Who wouldn't?' she smiled lovingly. 'I was sure I didn't care what you thought of that awful apartment, or of me, or of anything else, but something started happening from that very moment of you casting your eyes around the flat.' She paused, and as she looked into his love-filled eyes, she just had to ask, 'How about you?'

'When did I begin to fall in love with you?' he questioned, and smiled as, wanting her nearer to him still, he hugged her to him. With their faces close, he said, 'Thinking about it, I've realised that love must have been waiting for its cue from the first moment of eye-contact with you.'

'For you too?' Eden asked on a gasp.

'For me too, my lovely,' Sterne told her. 'Though, naturally, I was too hard-headed to ever believe in such occurrences.'

'Er—naturally,' she agreed, and would have agreed with him then if he had suddenly asserted that black was white.

'I was certain,' he went on to enlighten her, pausing to imprint a kiss on her cheek, 'that the only reason you appeared to fill more time in my head than any other female I've ever known was purely because no other female had ever tried to hit me before.'

'You thought about me—a lot,' Eden just had to fish.

'From the first,' he admitted happily. 'I knew you had no intention of getting in touch if you heard from your stepbrother or Camilla, but you were occupying my thoughts when suddenly the phone rang—and there you were.'

'I—er—wasn't going to ring,' she thought it only decent to confess.

'The point is, you did. And while I listened for any sign of mockery in your voice—the only nuance to come through was sincerity.'

Eden smiled as she told him, 'I lived to regret making that phone call.'

'When you discovered your car had a puncture?' he inserted with such an endearing grin that her love for him topped and overflowed. His grin had disappeared though when, reliving those minutes of them both on the pavement outside of the flat, he told her, 'You told me you were going to see a friend in Wales, and for the first time in my life, as I imagined your non-existent Welsh friend to be some male, I experienced jealousy.'

'You—were jealous!'

Sterne nodded. 'Not that I admitted it at the time. Only later, when your affection for your stepbrother started to niggle away at me, did I face the fact that I was jealous of any man you might care for.

'Oh, Sterne, don't be jealous of Thomas,' pleaded Eden.

'I'm not, my darling,' he assured her swiftly. 'I might still have envied him his closeness to you, but I ceased being jealous of him on the night I asked you about your feelings for him. I still didn't understand, though, why I should feel such relief when, coldly as I recall, you told me that your love for him was that of the sister which you truly felt you were to him.'

'You didn't know then—that you'd fallen...' an unexpected feeling of shyness made her break off.

'In love?' Sterne did not hesitate to finish for her. 'No, my dearest heart,' he went on, 'I still wasn't ready to face the question of why, contrary to my expectations, I should have enjoyed so much the fun-and-games caper you led me across the country in my search for Camilla.'

'You found it amusing too?' Eden asked, loving him with her eyes and wondering how much else they had enjoyed while pretending not to.

Gently he kissed her mouth. 'How could I not?' he asked simply. 'I started to grow more and more attracted to you with each passing incident. We'd lunched together on the motorway, and dined together that night at our hotel, and although I might have deluded myself that it was all in the good cause of keeping an eye on you, I all too soon started to lose sight of that fact.'

'You did!' She stared at him, wide-eyed.

'You'd charmed me that night,' Sterne told her.

'You'd done that to me!' Eden exclaimed, and by mutual unspoken consent, they embraced each other from the pure joy of sending all barriers crumbling.

'After dinner I took you to your room,' he resumed a minute later. He was looking down into her face when he added, 'I just had to kiss you.' He kissed her again, and when Eden had some breath back, and some trace of memory of what they had been talking of, she asked,

'It wasn't part of your scheme, then, to kiss me that night?'

Her cheeky grin seemed to delight Sterne, for he grinned too, as he confessed, 'I couldn't help myself. I didn't want to say goodnight there, Eden,' he added softly.

Her cheeks were slightly pink when she asked, 'You wanted to—come into my room.'

'Almost too late I remembered Camilla and why I was with you,' he revealed. 'My duty to her—to her father—had to come first. To lose my head without even knowing where she was would only complicate matters. Little did I know that within an hour of forcing myself to leave you, I should be back.'

'To tell me of the accident.'

'Yes,' he said, and, drawing a veil over the accident, he smiled tenderly at her as he added, 'We moved into Begonia Cottage and you, my dear love, began to torment and enchant me.'

'I *did*?'

'Minx that you are—you did,' he told her lovingly.

'How?' she just had to ask.

'For one, we'd hardly moved in and there you were running around in nothing but a towel,' he willingly supplied.

'From what I remember of that incident, you were coolly unimpressed,' Eden replied, and Sterne tapped her on the nose as he returned warmly,

'From what I remember, I was anything but cool. Why else do you think I found it so impossible to sleep that, in the middle of the night, I went back to the hotel to collect our gear?'

'You were afraid of losing your head?' Eden gasped.

'I was falling for you, but nowhere near ready to admit it,' he told her.

'When did you admit it?' she asked.

'I began to cave in,' he confessed cheerfully, 'on the day I came to see you when you were sitting with your stepbrother.'

'You came to see me? I thought you came to see Thomas!'

'I have to be honest with you, my dear,' Sterne replied. 'I gave your stepbrother no more thought than to know that where he was, I should find you. When I felt an irresistible compulsion to be near to you, I came looking.'

'That was the day you brought me here,' she recalled.

'That was the day, in this very spot, when I knew to my surprise, not to say astonishment, that I was on the brink of falling in love with you, and that I was powerless to stop it.'

'Is that what you meant—when you said "Life—is full of surprises"?'

There was a pleased look on Sterne's face that she had remembered something he had said, but he nodded, as he told her, 'It was too late. Before I knew it, I was caving in fast. I found I enjoyed laughing with you, seeing you laugh, hearing you laugh. You began to fascinate me so much that I could have spent hours just watching the changing expressions on your face.'

Eden sighed; everything that Sterne was saying was pure bliss. 'But you still hadn't admitted to yourself that you were actually in love with me?' she queried.

'I didn't know whether I was on my head or my heels over you,' he smiled. 'I knew that I liked you in every mood. Once you were in a sunny mood as I handed you a glass of wine,' he recalled, 'and more than anything else then, I wanted to kiss you.'

'I cooked dinner that night.' Eden remembered Sterne handing her a glass of wine. 'I thought I'd imagined something—suspended—something...!' she started to exclaim.

'You imagined nothing,' Sterne told her. 'I was so all over the place about you then that it took me all the time until you called me down to dinner to get myself under control.'

'That was the night you . . .' Suddenly, she halted. But it seemed that Sterne was not going to allow anything that might fret her to stay hidden in any dark corner.

'That was the night when, but for you remembering how, through me, your stepbrother had been hurt, you would have been mine, my dearest heart.'

'It wasn't really thoughts of Thomas that—er—got to me,' Eden felt bound to confess.

'It wasn't?'

Sterne's eyes were glued to her slightly embarrassed expression, as she told him truthfully, 'I sort of—just got cold feet—at the last moment.'

'Oh, my shy, nervous love!' he crooned, and seemed to understand completely how it had been with her, for he pulled her close up against his heart again.

'Was our l-lovemaking that night—the trifling physical interlude you said it was?' she couldn't refrain from asking.

'By no stretch of the imagination,' Sterne told her gently, and he planted a light kiss on her hair. 'So much happened for me that night—that was the night I admitted to myself that I was in love with you.'

'Oh, Sterne!' Eden breathed, and stretched up to kiss him.

'That was one hell of a night for me,' he murmured. 'I left the cottage early to walk around, and to try to get it all together. I phoned the hospital on my way back to the cottage, but as soon as I saw you again, I knew that the love I bore you wasn't something which my imagination had dreamed up.'

'You'd hoped that it was?'

'How could I hope for anything else?' he asked. 'You blamed me for what had happened to your stepbrother—the whole situation was intolerable. It was obvious that you were bitterly regretting what had taken place between us. Yet, even knowing that, I was so much in love with you that I didn't dare risk spending another night isolated in the same small dwelling with you.'

'Oh, darling,' she cried. 'Did that have anything to do with your decision to return to London?'

'It had everything to do with my returning to London,' he said candidly. 'I was impatient with you because you seemed more prone to hate me than anything else, and much more impatient with myself for the fact that, when solving problems has always come fairly easily to me, I should be floored to know how to get over this one.'

'I think I know something of the feeling,' Eden put in gently, and she confessed, 'It was as I was sitting beside Thomas's bed that same afternoon that I started to see things from your point of view. It wasn't long after that,' she admitted, 'that I realised that I was—in love with you.'

'You knew then! You knew when, because I couldn't keep away from you, I returned a couple of days later?'

Eden nodded, and nothing was said for long moments as Sterne bent his head to hers. Time hung suspended as they kissed and clung to each other, and Eden's cheeks were flushed again, her eyes shining, when at last they broke apart.

'You—er—returned—because of me?' she asked when a little of her thinking power had been recaptured.

Sterne looked down into her enchanted smiling face, and he too nodded, as he smiled and told her, 'Knowing for certain that I was going to book into a hotel that night, I left London at lunch time, the sooner to get to you.'

'But you didn't book into a hotel!'

'When it came to it,' he replied, his mouth turning up at the corners, 'I couldn't do it. I hadn't seen you for two whole days, and even the very frosty reception you gave me saw me unable to book into some hotel and risk not seeing you again before I returned to London.'

'I'm sorry about the frosty reception,' Eden apologised prettily, and was forgiven with a kiss, before Sterne went on to tell her,

'I was more crucified by the way we parted.'

'Don't remind me!' she shuddered and, remembering her own pain of that time, she told him, 'I don't know how we got started on that blazing row, but I was in a state of shock after you'd left.'

'My poor love,' he soothed, and held her tightly in his arms as he murmured, 'If it's any consolation, I felt as though I'd been pole-axed as I drove back to London that morning.' Eden was all attention as he recalled, 'We were both on our best behaviour to start with, but it didn't last.'

'You got uptight when I tried to tell you that Thomas really did love Camilla,' Eden slotted in.

'And you had my heart beating like a sledge-hammer when you told me that if Camilla had been compromised by staying in the cottage with him, *I*, by the same token, had compromised you.'

'You asked me if I was suggesting that you should offer to marry me,' Eden remembered.

'I hardly knew how to get my words out or if they were coming out in the right order,' Sterne confessed. 'All I knew then was that, by some miracle, I might have a glimmer of a chance to marry you. You soon—scornfully—set me straight on that issue,' he said solemnly.

'Am I forgiven?' she smiled.

'With a smile like that, you'd get away with murder,' he told her, his grin in evidence. He was serious again, though, when he asked her for forgiveness. 'I said some pretty foul things to you in return, my love. Though if it's any consolation I was sick at heart on that drive back to London in the belief that you truly hated me.'

More minutes of silence elapsed while Eden, as though to salve the hurt he had endured, kissed him, and was thrilled by his ardour when he returned her kiss with interest.

'So you don't hate me!' he muttered when at last he pulled back from her warm response.

Eden felt chokey again, and she shook her head, and her emotions were running high when she told him from her heart, 'I'm so glad that Camilla was married today. I'm so glad that you went to see her married. I'm so glad that...' Something in his expression caused her to break off.

'Confession time,' he said, and thrilled her even more when he owned, 'My duty to Camilla ended on her eighteenth birthday. But while I might have pretended to myself that I had a duty to go and see her married, *that*, my sweet love, was not the reason I came north today.'

'It wasn't?' she questioned.

'Naturally I care what happens to my old friend's daughter,' he acknowledged, 'but my main reason for being at that church today was not to see her married, but the hope of seeing you.'

Starry-eyed, Eden gazed at him. 'But—you left—before...'

'I couldn't stay,' Sterne told her. 'Not when I'd observed you from as close as I could. Your dear face as you absorbed the ceremony was a picture of loving feeling,' he said quietly. 'It was in such stark contrast to the hate-filled look you had for me the last time we met that I knew I'd deluded myself totally to have ever imagined that you had a—softer feeling for me.'

'Oh, darling,' Eden cried, but as the remarks sank in, she asked, 'You thought you'd seen my softer feelings for you? I thought I'd covered up how I truly felt about you very well.'

'You did,' he said, 'but I couldn't help but linger over the times when it wasn't all hate. We'd laughed and loved together,' he went on. 'All useless, of course, for memory of your hate would soon butt in to prevent me from getting in touch with you. It was that memory,' he added, 'which saw me labouring all hours in an attempt to get you out of my system.'

'It didn't work?' she asked, loving him with all of her being.

'I don't know how I could ever have imagined that it might,' Sterne said drily, and promptly told her, 'You'll have to cancel your viewing appointment for this evening.'

'You're getting very bossy,' Eden replied lovingly, but she had to confess, 'Er—actually—I made it up.'

'You haven't an appointment to view a property tonight?'

She shook her head. 'I lied,' she owned happily.

'Little fibber,' Sterne scolded with a laugh, but he thrilled her when he went on to inform her, 'Your house-hunting days are over, my love. There's a stray snippet of information in my head that tells me it takes only three days to get a special licence. We could be married in four—with your new home just waiting for you.'

'You're going too fast!' Eden exclaimed, not wondering at his success in business if he dealt with everything else in this straight-line manner.

'So,' he said, and slowed down to itemise, 'after being married by special licence, we'll first have our honeymoon—then,' he smiled at the enraptured look on her face, 'we'll return and you can move in to take charge of your new home.'

Eden's heart was going like a trip-hammer as she asked tentatively, 'Can you afford the time off for a h-honeymoon—at such short notice?'

'I've put in so much time just lately,' Sterne replied, 'that I'm due for a long break.'

'Oh!' she said, and had not one single objection to make. 'Are you sure a special licence takes as long as three days?' she asked with wide-eyed innocence.

For long moments Sterne was arrested by her expression. 'God, I'm falling more and more in love with you by the second!' he breathed hoarsely and, gathering her close, he brought her to stand from the bench they shared. 'Let's get going,' he said urgently, 'there's no time to lose.'

With their arms about each other, Eden went where he led, which was towards the cluster of trees which had a pathway through to a car park. At the car park, he again pulled her close and looked deeply into her eyes before kissing her and, most reluctantly, releasing her to assist her inside his car.

They were speeding on the motorway towards London, when Eden suddenly remembered something. 'My car!' she gasped. 'I forgot all about my car!'

The road up ahead was clear. Sterne turned his head to look at her. 'So did I,' he grinned. 'See what love does to you?'

Eden grinned back. She hadn't a care in the world.